**Fundamentals of
Botany Series**

# Nonseed Plants: Second Edition
# Form and Function

## Fundamentals of Botany Series

edited by
William A. Jensen
University of California, Berkeley
Leroy G. Kavaljian
Sacramento State College

The Plant Cell
William A. Jensen, University of
California, Berkeley

Reproduction, Heredity, and Sexuality
Stanton A. Cook, University of Oregon

Nonseed Plants: Form and Function
William T. Doyle, University of California,
Santa Cruz

Vascular Plants: Form and Function
Frank B. Salisbury, Utah State University,
and Robert V. Parke,
Colorado State University

Plants, Man, and the Ecosystem
W. D. Billings, Duke University

Plants and Civilization
Herbert G. Baker, University of
California, Berkeley

Plant Variation and Classification
C. Ritchie Bell, University of North
Carolina

Evolution and Plants of the Past
Harlan C. Banks, Cornell University

# Nonseed Plants: Form and Function

**Second Edition**

William T. Doyle

University of California, Santa Cruz

Wadsworth Publishing Company, Inc.
Belmont, California

# Preface

*Nonseed Plants: Form and Function* provides an essential core of information for the beginning student who meets lower plants for the first time. All chapters have been revised in the light of our greatly increased knowledge of the nonseed plant in the last seven years. The role of the electron microscope in expanding our vision of their morphology and ultrastructure is reflected in the electron micrographs included in the illustrations. Data from biochemistry, physiology, and developmental studies is included in the discussion of the organisms and in establishing their evolutionary relationships. Although new material has been added to all chapters, there has been extensive reworking of those chapters (viruses and bacteria, fungi, slime molds, blue-green algae, and euglenoids) where the research has been most intensive. The features which proved particularly useful in the first edition, such as the summary of the evolutionary relationships at the end of the chapters, have been retained and refined. Furthermore, new illustrations have been added throughout, including some excellent electron micrographs, and virtually all line drawings have been elegantly redone.

Because the coverage of this second edition has been extended to include the nonseed-producing vascular plants, a change in title was necessitated. At this time, I would like to gratefully acknowledge the encouragement and constructive criticism of the many teachers and students who have used the first edition. I would like especially to thank Dr. Elizabeth Gantt, who read and made many valuable suggestions on the manuscript of the first edition. I also wish to express my gratitude to all who have kindly allowed me to use their illustrations in this book. Specific acknowledgment is found in the picture captions.

# Series
# Foreword

Because of the immensity and complexity of the field of botany, the great diversity of plants, and the many methods of plant study, the problem of how to present to the student the highlights of botanical knowledge gained over centuries is not easy to solve. The authors and editors of the volumes in this series believe that an understanding of plants—their parts, their activities, and their relationship to man—is of fundamental importance in appreciating the significance of life. To stress this concept, the form and function of plants, tissues, and cells are treated together. At all levels of organization, in each volume, information gathered by morphologists, physiologists, cytologists, taxonomists, geneticists, biochemists, and ecologists is combined.

Thus, in the volume on *The Plant Cell* by William A. Jensen, the structure and function of the various cell parts are discussed together—for example, mitochondria and respiration, photosynthesis and chloroplasts. The volume by Stanton A. Cook, *Reproduction, Heredity, and Sexuality*, combines the principles of genetics with the means of reproduction in the various plant groups. The present volume, *Nonseed Plants: Form and Function*, by William T. Doyle, and *Vascular Plants: Form and Function*, by Frank B. Salisbury and Robert V. Parke, cover the major plant groups and discuss the plants in terms of morphology, physiology, and biochemistry. The relation of plants, particularly vascular plants, to their environment, to each other, and to man is covered in *Plants, Man, and the Ecosystem* by W. D. Billings. The form and distribution of plants of the past and their relation to the concepts of evolution are considered by Harlan Banks in *Evolution and Plants of the Past*. Herbert G. Baker, in *Plants and Civilization,* discusses the importance of plants to man's social and economic development and the equally important consideration of man's role in the modification and distribution of plants.

In a series such as this, the editors are faced with the task of dividing a broad field into areas that can be presented in a meaningful way by the authors. There must be logic in the entire scheme, with few gaps and a minimum of overlap. Yet an instructor may not want to use the series of volumes in the sequence and manner preferred by the editors. Consequently, each volume must be usable alone and also in any sequence with the others. To achieve such a high degree of versatility is difficult, but we believe the series exhibits these features.

A concerted effort has been made by the authors and editors to maintain a consistent level of presentation. However, each author has been encouraged to approach his subject in his own way and to write in his own style in order to provide variety and to exploit the uniqueness of the individual author's viewpoint. Finally, while presenting the principles of botany we have tried to communicate the excitement of recent developments as well as the joy that comes with the extension of knowledge in any field.

**Series Foreword**

# Contents

Contents

Contents

# 1

## Introduction

Nonseed plants form a heterogeneous group that includes bacteria, fungi, algae, bryophytes, ferns, and the so-called fern allies. They are separated from seed plants by a single distinctive feature: they do not reproduce by seeds. Thus nonseed plants (like the invertebrates of the animal kingdom) are defined by negation, a conceptually unsatisfactory but occasionally useful procedure.

Nonseed plants are found in all environments capable of supporting life. They are in soil, water, and air, and they grow in desert and arctic regions as well as in cold mountain areas and hot springs. They have their most luxuriant development in tropical and subtropical regions where humidity is relatively high. Although nonseed plants are widely distributed as a group, the environmental tolerances of individual species are usually restricted. For example, a species of alga growing in hot springs will generally be found only in hot springs. Other algae may be found only in snow.

Nonseed plants are as diversified in form as they are in distribution. Many are unicellular and microscopic. Unicellular species exhibit great morphological diversity resulting from adaptation to their particular environment. Unbranched and branched chains of cells, called *filaments,* are also common body forms. The most highly differentiated nonseed plants possess leaves, stems, and roots. The giant seaweeds, which may grow to lengths of over 60 meters, are the largest nonseed plants, and are also longer than most seed plants.

### Relationship of Form to Function

It is impossible to divorce biological form from function, because form is the physical expression of function. Multicellularity in plants leads to the division of labor among component cells — in other words, to cell specialization for function. Thus a multicellular moss is differentiated into leaflike, stemlike, and rootlike portions. Component cells of the moss plant are specialized for photosynthesis, water conduction, water absorption, food storage, or strengthening.

Unicellular organisms are simple in form and structure only; they are functionally as complex as multicellular organisms. Each free-living unicell is capable of the vital functions characteristic of multicellular plants — growth, metabolism, and reproduction.

(Because the long-term survival of species depends on their comparative success in reproduction, it is not surprising to find that the reproductive structures of many nonseed plants are highly specialized and adapted to particular environmental conditions.)

### Classification

There are approximately 400,000 known seed and nonseed plants.[1] Without some means of classification or ordering, the amount of information would be overwhelming.

The species is the basic unit, or *taxon,* of classification. Species, in turn, are grouped into genera, and the scientific name of an organism consists of both the generic and the specific name. The scientific name is written in italics (or underlined), and the first letter of the generic name is capitalized. In this manner, the scientific name of a maidenhair fern is written *Adiantum capillus-veneris.* The main categories used in plant classification are: kingdom, division, class, order, family, genus, and species. The kingdom is the highest level of classification. (The term "phylum," which customarily follows "kingdom" and is widely used in zoological classification, is not recognized as a category by the International Code of Botanical Nomenclature and should not be used in botanical classification. The categories "phylum" and "division" have slightly different meanings; they are not comparable or interchangeable terms.)

Two general types of classification are used in biology. The oldest type, called *artificial,* is one in which organisms are grouped together on the basis of convenience. Distinction between groups is primarily based on a single charac-

---

[1] This tremendous diversity of plant types is explained by evolution. Organisms can, and have, changed with time. Evolution also means that organisms living today were derived from pre-existing organisms. Evolution thus not only explains diversities, it also explains similarities between organisms.

teristic, such as whether they are evergreen or deciduous, whether or not they form seeds, or whether or not they possess a vascular (conducting) system. This type of classification, used by many early botanists, serves more to analyze than to classify organisms. In recent years, attempts have been made to eliminate from classification systems those groups which are based only on differences in single sets of characters.

In *natural* classifications, on the other hand, organisms are grouped according to overall likeness. The organisms within a group have a high degree of similarity. No single character is considered to be of paramount importance; the organisms have a combination of characters in common. The need for classification schemes to reflect evolutionary relationships has been stated by many biologists. A *phylogenetic* system is a natural classification system based on data derived from both fossil and extant plants. A true phylogenetic classification is based on a complete evolutionary series, which is rare in the fossil record; therefore, any attempt to erect a definitive phylogenetic classification is foredoomed. In practice, most natural systems are in part phylogenetic and in part *phenetic*. A completely phenetic system is one in which organisms are grouped according to *overall similarity* with no specific consideration of possible evolutionary relationships.

It is important to remember that classification schemes are man-made and are based (1) on the amount and kind of information available, and (2) on how these data are evaluated. It is also important to note that, in general, data obtained in the past are still valid today, and will remain valid in the future. For example, organisms of a particular species of alga that had two flagella 50 years ago will still have two flagella when investigated today or 50 years from now. This type of information can be obtained again and again, and does not change. However, new information is constantly available and phylogenetic and phenetic conclusions derived from the data may change. Moreover, investigators may interpret the same data differently; hence, the existence of several different classifications.

What kinds of information are used to identify the major groups of plants? Of prime importance are data concerning the cellular level of organization. The major groups of algae have long been identified on the basis of photosynthetic pigments, food reserve, flagellation, nuclear behavior, and general structure of the cell. In this book, these same criteria are applied to all plants; the plants are grouped according to the relative importance of correlated characters. Three of the characters most useful in grouping are described in more detail below (and are summarized in the Appendix).

### Pigmentation

Many plants are photosynthetic. In order for light energy to be trapped and made available for photosynthesis, molecules capable of energy absorption must be present in the cell. These molecules are not the same in all plants. Chlorophylls, phycobiliproteins, and fucoxanthin (a carotenoid) are kinds of *pigment molecules* that absorb light in photosynthesis. Several different types of chlorophyll molecules are known; at least four types occur in bacteria and four in other plants. However, no organism has more than two types of chlorophyll, some have only one, and others have none. The distribution of the various types of chlorophyll, phycobiliprotein, and fucoxanthin is used as a clue in identifying related plants.

### Food Reserve

Food that is not immediately needed for growth or cell maintenance is commonly stored as proteins, lipids, or carbohydrates. (Little is known about the comparative chemistry of protein or lipid reserves, and they will not be discussed here.) Several different kinds of carbohydrate food reserves have been identified in plants. Most of them contain glucose (dextrose) as the basic building unit, and they differ in their linkage characteristics ($\alpha$ or $\beta$ configurations), chain lengths, or branching patterns (see Appendix for details). True starch (which stains blue when an iodine solution is added) is one type of carbohydrate; glycogen is another. If there are different kinds of polysaccharides constructed from similar building blocks, the presence of different cellular control mechanisms is indicated. Organisms with a similar polysaccharide food reserve most likely possess similar control mechanisms. The type of food reserve, then, is an additional criterion useful in identifying related plants.

### Flagellation

Many plants either are flagellated in the adult state or have flagellated reproductive cells. Flagella have two basic structures. One type, found only in bacteria, consists of a single major fibril in cross section (Fig. 1-1a). On the other hand, nine peripheral and two central fibrils are found in a cross section of the other flagellar type (Fig. 1-1b). Each of the nine peripheral fibrils, in turn, consists of two subfibrils. The presence of nine peripheral and two central fibrils (the 9 + 2 arrangement) is characteristic of all plant flagella (other than those of bacteria) and of animal flagella and cilia. Flagella of the 9 + 2 type have two common forms: whiplash and tinsel (Fig. 1-1c). Tinsel flagella possess lateral, filiform appendages, and whiplash flagella lack them.

The structure, form, number, and manner of insertion (anterior, posterior, or lateral) of flagella are important in identifying groups of related plants.

By the evaluation and consistent application of kinds of data described above, plants may be grouped as indicated in Table 1-1. This classification scheme reflects the author's current views concerning plant relationships, and undoubtedly will undergo modification in the future as additional infor-

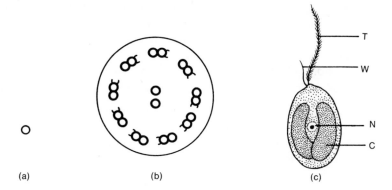

**Figure 1-1.** (a) Cross section of bacterial flagellum showing a single fibril. (b) Cross section of a flagellum with a 9 + 2 arrangement of fibrils. Note that the bacterial flagellum is of the same approximate size in section as a single central fibril of a 9 + 2 flagellum. (c) Flagellated cell (*Ochromonas*, a golden alga) with a tinsel flagellum (T), whiplash flagellum (W), nucleus (N), and chloroplast (C).

**Table 1-1.** Plant classification

| Common Name | Taxonomic Category |
|---|---|
| Plants | Kingdom Plantae |
| Bacteria | Division Schizophyta* |
| Fungi | Division Eumycota* |
| Slime molds | Division Myxomycota |
| Blue-green algae | Division Cyanophyta |
| Red algae | Division Rhodophyta |
| Golden algae and diatoms | Division Chrysophyta |
| Brown algae | Division Phaeophyta |
| Dinoflagellates | Division Pyrrophyta |
| Yellow-green algae | Division Xanthophyta |
| Euglenoids | Division Euglenophyta |
| Green plants | Division Chlorophyta |
| Green algae | Sub-division Chlorophycophytina* |
| Land plants | Sub-division Embryophytina |
| Mosses and liverworts | Class Bryopsida* |
| Psilopsids | Class Psilopsida |
| Lycopsids | Class Lycopsida |
| Horsetails and sphenopsids | Class Sphenopsida |
| Ferns | Class Pteropsida |
| Seed plants | Class Spermopsida |
| Gymnosperms | Sub-class Gymnospermidae* |
| Angiosperms | Sub-class Angiospermidae |

*The Division, Sub-division, Class, and Sub-class endings are in accordance with those suggested by the International Code of Botanical Nomenclature.

mation becomes available. This scheme differs from other classifications (such as the one by Bold, cited in Suggestions for Further Reading) primarily by the inclusion of green algae and all the land plants in the same division. Most botanists consider that the land plants evolved from green algae, or at least had a common ancestry with them. I view green algae and land plants as forming a natural and distinct group, and therefore think that their classification in the same division is justified. The green algae and land plants differ primarily in their levels of organization. Somewhat similar diversity in levels of organization of the plant body occurs within both brown and red algal groups (see later). (The relationship of the green algae to the land plants will be discussed again in Chapter 11.)

A glance at the classification scheme used in this volume shows that the nonseed plants have representatives in all divisions of plants. This means that they have tremendous diversity in form, function, and physiology. We will explore some of this diversity in the following chapters.

# 2

## Viruses and Bacteria

Viruses will be discussed briefly here, even though they are not considered to be plants. Viruses have such considerable economic importance that everyone should be aware of them and of the research being done on them. Remarkable advances in molecular biology have been made possible because of the experimental utility of these organisms.

### Viruses

Viruses are extremely small, ranging from 2 to 20 microns in diameter. They are discovered and described as *pathogens* (agents that cause disease). Because viruses are so small, their presence in an organism is detected only by their effect upon the host, and the host's response is so specific that a virus is usually named after the type of disease it produces. Viruses cause diseases in a variety of organisms, from bacteria to flowering plants and man. Among the flowering plants viruses probably rank second only to the fungi as agents of diseases of economic importance. Crops such as potatoes, beans, sugar beets, peaches, tomatoes, and tobacco are susceptible to virus diseases. Viral diseases of man include poliomyelitis, influenza, smallpox, and certain types of cancer.

Host specificity is one of the most characteristic features of viruses. Usually a single kind of virus infects and multiplies in only one type of host. Moreover, most viruses grow only in specific tissues or organs within the host. The basis for this specificity is variable, and in most cases it is not well understood. Insects that feed upon plants, especially sucking insects like aphids, are the most important means of transmitting viruses from plant to plant under natural conditions. Exceptions to narrow host specificity are found in some of the plant viruses that are carried by insect vectors. In some instances, the virus has been shown to multiply in both the plant and insect tissues. Insects also are important in the transmission of some of man's viral diseases, such as yellow fever.

Since viruses are too small to be seen with the aid of the light microscope, for a long time they were known only as filterable (passing through a filter which prevents passage of most kinds of bacteria), disease-producing organisms. Thanks to the electron microscope (with its resolution down to 10 Å or less) and modern research techniques, we now know much more about their morphology, structure, development, and genetics. Only a little of what we know, however, will be explored in the following sections.

### General Characteristics

Viruses exist in two distinct states, an extracellular state and an intracellular state. In the extracellular state, the virus is lifeless; it possesses no respiratory system of its own nor does it reproduce. This is the state of the mature virus particle, called the *virion*. Virions have relatively simple forms and structures. Commonly they are brick-shaped, spherical, rod-shaped, or needle-shaped. Some of the *bacteriophages* (viruses that infect bacteria) are more complex, being differentiated into a head, tail, and tail fibers (Fig. 2-1).

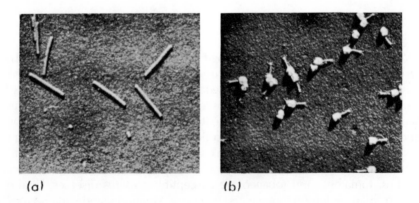

(a)     (b)

**Figure 2-1.** Mature virus particles (virions). (a) Tobacco mosaic virus. (b) T₄ bacteriophage of *Escherichia coli*. Note head, tail, and tail fibers. Courtesy of the Virus Laboratory, University of California, Berkeley.

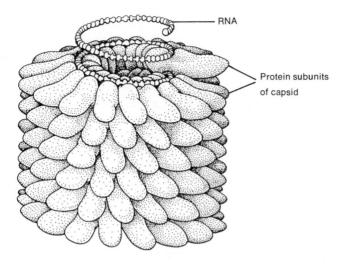

RNA

Protein subunits
of capsid

**Figure 2-2.** Tobacco mosaic virus. Diagram of portion of virion to show relationship of protein sub-units of the capsid to the helical RNA molecule. Courtesy of Dr. D. L. D. Caspar, Children's Cancer Research Foundation, Inc., Boston.

Virions consist of two main parts: an outer protein coat, called the *capsid,* and a nucleic acid core. Unlike other organisms, which have both DNA and RNA, a virus contains only one kind of nucleic acid, either DNA or RNA. In most cases little is known about how the nucleic acid is packed inside the capsid. The tobacco mosaic virus (TMV) is an exception, however, and the relationship of RNA to the capsid is shown in Fig. 2-2. The nucleic acid in the capsid may be either single- or double-stranded. It is double-stranded in most of the DNA-containing viruses, but single-stranded in most of those containing RNA. In addition to nucleic acid and protein, some of the larger viruses contain a few molecules of lipids, carbohydrates, and enzymes.

Many animal and a few plant viruses have an envelope external to the capsid. In some cases the envelope represents the plasma membrane of the host-cell, which is formed around the capsid as the virion emerges through the membrane of the animal cell surface. The envelopes of these virions possibly function to facilitate entry into new host-cells, and thereby account for some of the specificity characteristic of viruses. In other cases, the envelopes are formed around the virion while it is still completely inside the host cytoplasm.

A striking feature of mature virions of many viruses is that they can be crystallized from purified solutions. The crystals can then be dissolved in water, and the particles used to reinfect the host. The ability to form crystals indicates that virions have an orderly structure.

---

**Viruses and Bacteria**                                                    **9**

Although a mature virion consists primarily of a protein capsid and a nucleic acid core, the entry into the host-cell of the nucleic acid alone is sufficient to establish infection. Support for this statement comes from studies with the tobacco mosaic virus (TMV) (Fig. 2-1a; 2-2) in which the protein coat can be removed and separated from the RNA. Subsequent infection by the naked RNA results in the formation of new virions by the host, complete with new protein capsids. However, the degree of infection is considerably lower when using naked TMV RNA. This suggests that the capsid might serve to protect the nucleic acid, or that it somehow facilitates the entry of the nucleic acid into the host cell, or both.

The mechanism by which the viral nucleic acid enters the host-cell is variable. In some cases, such as in the bacteriophages, the nucleic acid is injected directly into the cell through the host-cell wall; the capsid remains outside the cytoplasm. In other cases, the envelope interacts with the plasma membrane of the host-cell and the enveloped virion enters the cytoplasm intact. Here, the viral nucleic acid is released later into the cytoplasm. Although a single virion generally is sufficient to initiate infection, more than one virion may infect a single cell. Moreover, more than one kind of virus can infect a single cell at the same time. When this happens, the host-cell may produce two kinds of virions at the same time.

All dynamic events (including the biosynthesis of new viral material) occur during the intracellular state of the virus. The virus genome functions as a piece of genetic material that, when introduced into the host-cell, is capable of redirecting the biosynthetic machinery of the host-cell so that the cell makes virus material. The formation of new virus material is at the expense of the host-cell's metabolism, hence the characteristic virus-induced disease symptoms mentioned earlier. The virus is dependent upon the host-cell for nucleotides needed to produce new viral nucleic acid, amino acids for proteins, the protein-synthesizing machinery itself, and a supply of energy. Thus the virus can be considered to be an obligate intracellular parasite in that it requires a living host for the formation of new virions.

Results from numerous genetic studies, utilizing mutations and recombinations in DNA-containing bacteriophages, indicate that the virus DNA contains linearly arranged genes. The viral DNA corresponds to a single chromosome of other organisms. The viral DNA also functions in the normal manner, serving as a template for the formation of messenger RNA (mRNA). The nucleic acid of RNA-containing viruses, like TMV, also contain all the information needed for the formation of new virus particles. In this case, the genetic information is contained in the base sequences of the RNA molecule. There is some evidence that viral RNA acts directly as mRNA in the host-cell. At least viral RNA of some viruses has been shown to form *in vitro* polysomes with host-cell ribosomes.

The reproduction of viruses differs from that of all other organisms in that there is no growth in size followed by division. Rather, reproduction occurs by *replication* of the nucleic acid and its incorporation into a new capsid. Moreover, replication of viral nucleic acid is not associated with the biosynthesis of the proteins specific to the capsid, since nucleic acid replication continues even when protein synthesis has been inhibited experimentally. Normally the synthesis of viral protein begins some time after the start of nucleic acid replication. The formation of mature virions serves to remove the nucleic acid from the cytoplasm, and the nucleic acid generally is not released back into the cytoplasm of the same cell.

### Bacteriophages

Bacteriophages are extremely useful research organisms and have been used to magnificent advantage in molecular biology. Both the phages and the bacteria have short generation times, both are easy to handle experimentally, and the bacteria can be grown readily under controlled, reproducible conditions. Researchers have used bacteriophages in studying how the virus enters the host-cell, how viral nucleic acid affects the host's metabolism, viral replication, viral genetic systems, and viral morphogenesis. For these reasons, the bacteriophage-host relationship has been selected for discussion in greater detail.

Bacteriophages vary considerably in size and form. The largest forms are remarkably complex, differentiated into head, tail, and tail fibers that serve as organs of attachment to the host-cell surface. One such virion, known as phage $T_4$, is shown in Figs. 2-1b and 2-4. The $T_4$ phage is one of several *coliphages,* so named because they attack cells of *Escherichia coli,* a bacterium common in the intestine of man. The nucleic acid of most bacteriophages is DNA (Fig. 2-3); only a few RNA-containing phages are known.

Detection of phages in a culture of bacteria most commonly results because of the *lysis* (dissolution) of the infected bacterial cells, accompanied by the release of newly formed virions. A common method of initiating infection in experimental studies is to mix susceptible bacteria and phage together in a suspension and then to spread this mixture evenly over the surface of a nutrient agar medium in a Petri dish. The phage will infect cells, and in a short period of time these infected cells lyse and release newly formed phage virions into the medium. In this manner the phages infect more and more cells. Clear areas, called *plaques,* appear on the surface of the medium, representing localized areas of cell lysis. The number of plaques per Petri dish indicates the intensity of infection. Moreover, plaque morphology generally is characteristic for a specific phage, and thereby provides a useful marker in phage genetic studies.

During infection the phage virions stick to the bacterial cell wall by means of the protein coat in tailless forms and by means of the tail structure in virions

---

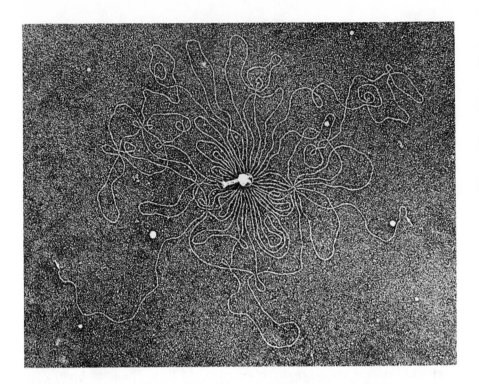

**Figure 2-3.** Single DNA macromolecule released from osmotically shocked $T_2$ bacteriophage. Note free ends of molecule at arrows (lower left and right center of photo). Courtesy of Dr. A. K. Kleinschmidt, New York University School of Medicine. Reproduced from *Biochem. Biophys. Acta*, 61:681, Fig. 1 (1962) by permission from Elsevier Publishing Company.

with tails. The tail fibers are the primary structures of attachment in those phages that have them. However, the tail cannot attach at every place on the cell surface. The ability to attach depends upon the presence of specific receptor sites on the bacterial wall, and the tail fibers must be in the proper configuration for attachment to these sites. For example, the tail fibers of phage $T_4$ must be extended in order for attachment to occur, and extension depends upon the presence of magnesium ions and the amino acid tryptophan in the culture medium. It is also possible to obtain mutant bacteria that are resistant to phage infection because of a change in the configuration of the receptor sites. Conversely, phage mutants with altered tail structures may lose their ability to attach to the cell surface. The exact nature of the phage-receptor site interaction is still unclear.

The attachment of the phage to the bacterial cell and the injection of the phage nucleic acid into the host-cell have been relatively well studied in coliphage $T_4$. In this virus, attachment is made by the tail fibers and the pronged

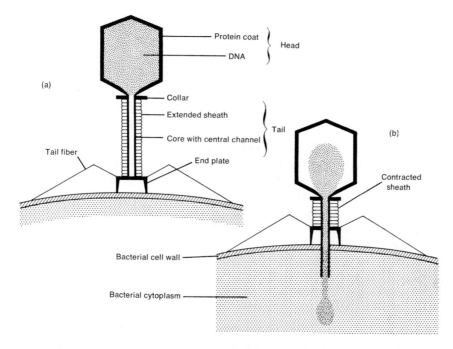

Protein coat ⎤
          ⎬ Head
DNA ⎦

(a)

Collar

Extended sheath ⎤
              ⎬ Tail
Core with central channel ⎦

Tail fiber

End plate

(b)

Contracted sheath

Bacterial cell wall

Bacterial cytoplasm

**Figure 2-4.** Schematic representation of coliphage $T_4$ virion and its component parts. (a) Virion attached to the surface of the bacterial wall and prior to contraction of sheath proteins. Only two of the six tail fibers shown. Spikes of the end plate are appressed to the bacterial wall. (b) Virion with tail sheath contracted, and the DNA partially injected into the cytoplasm of the bacterial cell. Drawings based on Simon and Anderson, *Virology*, 32:279 (1967).

end plate of the tail (Fig. 2-4a). A hole is then dissolved in the bacterial wall, presumably by a phage enzyme. Contraction of the sheath proteins (a process apparently similar to muscle contraction) then forces the hollow inner core of the tail piece through the wall and the nucleic acid (DNA in $T_4$) is injected into the cell (Fig. 2-4b). The empty phage capsid remains outside the cell wall. What happens next in the phage-host relation depends upon the kind of phage and the culture conditions.

There are two general kinds of phage-bacterium relationships: *lytic* and *lysogenic*. In the lytic relationship the phage induces rapid cell death, causing the cell that it attacked, or its immediate descendents, to lyse. The phages involved in the lytic relationship are called *intemperate,* or *virulent.* The viral nucleic acid of virulent phages almost immediately takes over the biosynthetic machinery of the bacterial cell. This may or may not be accompanied by a breakdown of the DNA of the host cell. The sequence of events that occurs after nucleic acid injection has been well documented in the $T_4$ coliphage. With this virus, breakdown of the bacterial DNA occurs within one minute

---

after infection and the first new viral DNA is detected within five minutes. The first mature virions are found in 13 minutes after infection, and by 25 minutes approximately 200 virions occur in the cell. An enzyme called lysozyme appears in the cell during the later stages of virion formation. The action of this enzyme results in lysis of the cell wall accompanied by release of the newly formed virions into the medium. The sequence of infection leading to cell lysis is diagrammed in Fig. 2-5.

The formation of virions as complex as the $T_4$ phage presents interesting problems in morphogenesis. Each of the three main units (head, tail, and tail fibers) is synthesized independently; that is, there are separate head, tail, and tail fiber pools within the cell. The fully formed separate units are then hooked together to make the mature virion. The tail unit, complete with collar and end plate, becomes attached (apparently spontaneously) to a head unit, with enclosed viral nucleic acid. The attachment of the tail fibers to the end plate is the final step in $T_4$ morphogenesis. The syntheses of head, tail, and tail fiber units occur independently of each other, and at the time of cell lysis the extra virus parts are also released. In recent years the genetic control of the stages in viral morphogenesis has been under active study by a number of scientists.

In the lysogenic relationship the virus genome is carried by the bacterium from cell generation to generation with only occasional cell lysis and release of new virions. The bacteriophages that are involved in the lysogenic relationship are referred to as *temperate* phages. The bacterial cells that contain temperate phages grow normally and, except for occasional cell lysis, there is little to indicate that the cells contain viral nucleic acid. In *Escherichia coli* the viral genome is physically attached to the host chromosome. In this form the viral genome is called a *prophage*. Most of the viral genes are not functioning in the prophage state. However, a shift from the lysogenic to the lytic state can be induced by a variety of agents. For example, ultraviolet light is a powerful inducing agent for many kinds of prophages. In lysogeny, then, the viral genome enters a susceptible bacterial cell and, instead of causing the immediate synthesis of new virions, the viral nucleic acid becomes attached to the bacterial chromosome. In this state, the prophage condition, the viral genome is replicated as part of the bacterial chromosome and is passed on with the chromosome from generation to generation. This remains a relatively stable relationship until it is upset by an external inducer, such as ultraviolet light. Upon induction, the genes of the viral genome become active and redirect the biosynthetic machinery of the cell. New virions are formed and the cell lyses.

Most of the major discoveries and basic concepts about the virus-host relationship have come from studies on the bacteriophages, because of their experimental utility. The concepts have been extended and confirmed in viruses of other plants and animals, although the same kind of simple, clear-cut experiments have generally not been as easy to perform. In this regard, cell

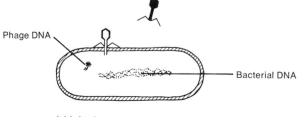

Phage DNA

Bacterial DNA

(a) Infection

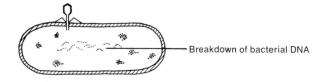

Breakdown of bacterial DNA

(b) Viral DNA replication

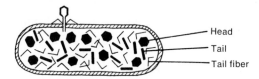

Head

Tail

Tail fiber

(c) Synthesis of phage parts

(d) Assembly of phage particles

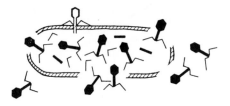

(e) Cell lysis

**Figure 2-5.** Developmental cycle of a virulent coliphage. The phage particles and bacterial cells are not drawn to scale.

---

**Viruses and Bacteria**

and tissue culture techniques have proven increasingly useful. There are still many details of the virus-host relation that we do not understand, and it is to be expected that many important discoveries will result from future research.

### Bacteria

Bacteria, or Schizophyta (schizo = fission; phyton = plant), are extremely common soil organisms, and they are also abundant in the air, on skin, plants, and animals, and in fresh and salt water. Since most bacteria are less than 9 microns in length and are readily blown about by the wind, they are often troublesome airborne contaminants. Bacteria have been collected several miles above the earth. The great economic importance of bacteria, which stimulated a considerable amount of research, has contributed to the separation of the study of bacteria from botany, resulting in the establishment of departments of bacteriology in many universities. Bacteriologists are employed by federal, state, and local health agencies, universities, hospitals, sanitation and water departments, and chemical drug companies.

The variety of forms of bacteria is limited, in contrast to their physiological potential. Among the true bacteria three shapes are common: spheres (Cocci), rods (Bacilli), and helices (Spirillum) (Fig. 2-6). The cells of some bacteria form colonies of characteristic shape. Others, such as the actinomycetes, are filamentous. Although of simple form, bacteria are physiologically diverse, and the identification of species usually depends on studies of the metabolic char-

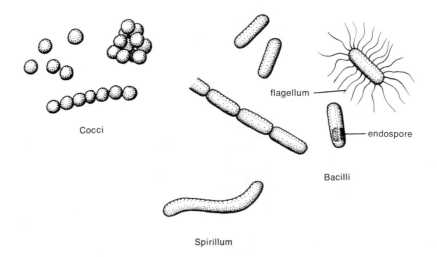

**Figure 2-6.** Various shapes of bacterial cells.

acteristics of populations of bacteria in culture. These investigations involve *axenic* (only one kind of organism present) culturing of bacteria in liquid or on solidified media. Most bacteria are *aerobic* organisms (requiring the presence of molecular oxygen for growth). Other bacteria can live in the complete absence of oxygen, and may even be inhibited in growth by its presence. These are the *anaerobic* bacteria, and they are present wherever putrifaction occurs.

Bacteria were discovered only after the invention of the microscope. Because of their small size, near the limits of resolution of the light microscope, little could be described of their cellular structure until relatively recently. Use of the electron microscope, along with suitable (and still improving) fixation procedures, have enabled us to learn much more about their cellular structure. A little of this knowledge will be explored in the next section.

### Cellular Structure

The most striking feature of bacterial cells is their almost complete absence of membranous profiles. All double unit membrane organelles — such as mitochondria, nuclei, and chloroplasts — are absent. Functional groups of enzymes are not compartmentalized in cell organelles; the whole cell itself is the basic functional unit. This type of cellular organization is considered to be primitive, and has been termed *prokaryotic* (pro = before; karyon = nucleus of a cell). Only the bacteria and blue-green algae have this type of cellular organization. Organisms that possess double unit membrane-enclosed structures (mitochondria, nuclei, and chloroplasts) are termed *eukaryotic* (eu = good). It is of interest that most bacterial cells are smaller than nuclei and chloroplasts, and are about the same size as mitochondria.

Although mitochondria are absent, the respiratory enzymes in bacteria are membrane-bound, being associated with the cell membrane (also called plasma membrane or plasmalemma). Localized infolding of the cell membrane gives rise to a structure called a *mesosome* (mesos = in the middle; soma = body) (Fig. 2-7).

The relatively membrane-free cytoplasm of an actively growing bacterial cell is packed with ribosomes. The ribosomes lie free in the cytoplasm, since the cell lacks an endoplasmic reticulum. Bacterial ribosomes resemble in structure and in chemical composition ribosomes of other organisms. They differ, however, in that bacterial ribosomes are smaller and thus sediment at a slower rate in a density gradient than do the cytoplasmic ribosomes of eukaryotic organisms. (The sedimentation rate of blue-green algal ribosomes is similar to that of bacteria.) Some of the ribosomes form clusters, called polyribosomes or polysomes, which are active in protein synthesis (see Jensen, *The Plant Cell*, this series).

The DNA, not delimited from the cytoplasm by a nuclear envelope, occurs in the central region of the cell (Fig. 2-7). This region stains deeply with dyes

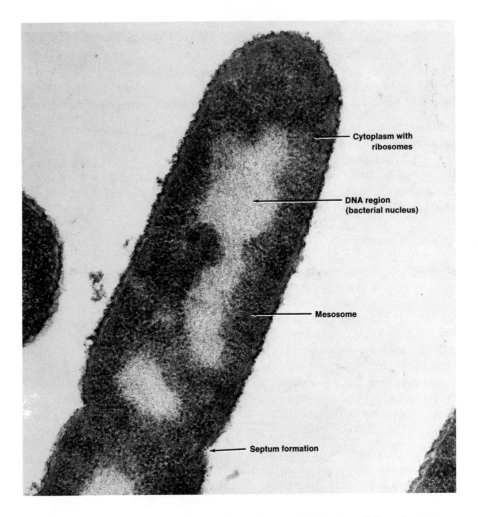

Cytoplasm with
ribosomes

DNA region
(bacterial nucleus)

Mesosome

Septum formation

**Figure 2-7.**  Electronmicrograph of *Escherichia coli*. Note the association of the meso-some, an infolding of the cell membrane, with the nucleus and with septum formation. Courtesy of Dr. R. D. Pontefract, Department of National Health and Welfare, Ottawa, Canada.

for DNA and has been termed the bacterial nucleus (or nucleoplasm). Genetic evidence shows that each nucleus contains a single linkage group and effectively acts as a single chromosome. During cell division each nucleus behaves as a unit, but the chromatin does not become tightly coiled and therefore is not obviously chromosomal at any time, nor does a spindle form.

The details of division of the bacterial nucleus are under investigation. Studies have indicated that the bacterial chromosome is attached at one site to the cell membrane, and there is evidence that the mesosome serves as the connection between the chromosome and the cell membrane. The association of mesosomes with the place of septum formation (Fig. 2-7) has led to the suggestion that they are involved in nuclear separation during cell division. Pontefract et al. (see Selected Readings) have put forward the hypothesis that in *Escherichia coli* the DNA of the cell and the newly synthesized DNA are each attached to a separate, polar mesosome. Cell wall biosynthesis in *E. coli* has been shown to occur in the central region of the cell, and Pontefract et al. suggest that the attachment of the nuclei to polar mesosomes would mechanically effect separation of sister genomes during cell growth. This is then followed by septum formation (Fig. 2-7). Additional research will indicate whether this type of nuclear division is widespread in bacteria.

Some bacteria (e.g., *Escherichia coli*) are capable of nuclear exchange followed by a type of gene segregation. This sexual phenomenon differs from that in eukaryotic organisms in that the nuclear material is exchanged only in one direction, and only a part of the nuclear material normally is transferred. When two bacterial cells come together, the process is called *conjugation*. One cell acts as the donor and the other as the recipient (Fig. 2-8).

The bacterial protoplast is surrounded by a wall that is chemically diverse. Carbohydrates, proteins, and lipids are all present. Cellulose (in cell walls of most plants) and chitin (in cell walls of some algae and fungi, and in some insects) are not present, although a few bacteria secrete cellulose into the environment. Differences in the chemical structure of bacteria have enabled bacteriologists to separate bacteria into two large groups: gram-positive bacteria, the cell walls of which turn purple in the presence of the Gram's stain, and gram-negative ones that do not retain the purple coloration. The Gram's stain is widely used in the identification of bacteria.

The form of the bacterial cell appears to depend on the presence of the cell wall. It is possible to isolate the protoplast from the wall, for example, by dis-

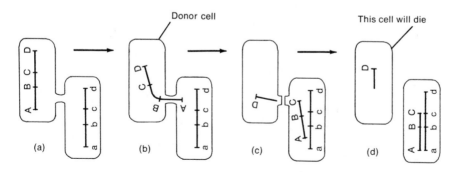

**Figure 2-8.** Conjugation type of sexuality in *Escherichia coli.* Note that only a portion of the chromosome is transferred, and that the donor cell, with an incomplete chromosome, will die.

---

**Viruses and Bacteria**

solving the wall with the enzyme lysozyme. The resultant naked protoplast has a spherical form even though it may have been derived from a rod-shaped bacterium. With the use of other enzymes, protoplasts have been obtained from fungi (such as yeasts and the mold *Neurospora*) and a liverwort (*Marchantia*). Fungi and liverwort protoplasts appear to escape through pores in the cell wall that develop prior to the complete dissolution of the wall. These protoplasts too are spherical in shape. On the other hand, the cell wall, minus the enclosed protoplast, retains its normal shape. Thus one may conclude that the wall, not the protoplast, determines the form of the cell. Isolated protoplasts are quite sensitive to osmotic shock, and the osmotic pressure of the medium must be adjusted in order to maintain the protoplasts. On the other hand, protoplasts surrounded by an intact wall can withstand a wide range of osmotic pressures. The presence of a wall appears to be advantageous to cell survival in a changing environment. An interesting aspect of protoplast physiology is that naked protoplasts are unable to synthesize a new wall. Moreover, they are incapable of multiplication. The significance of this is not yet fully understood.

Cell division generally occurs by the centripetal ingrowth of a crosswall perpendicular to the long axis of the cell in nonspherical bacteria. This ingrowth divides the cell into approximately equal daughter cells. A mesosome is often closely associated with the place of septum formation. Subsequent cell enlargement is due primarily to protein synthesis; no aqueous vacuole is present. Nonseparation of daughter cells results in the formation of filaments or colonies.

A slime layer that helps prevent the cell from drying out is usually present external to the wall. A thick, rigid slime layer is called a *capsule*. In bacteria such as those that cause pneumonia (*Klebsiella pneumoniae*) and tuberculosis (*Mycobacterium tuberculosis*), the slime layer seems to afford protection against body defense mechanisms.

Bacterial flagella, as indicated in Chapter 1, are not equivalent to flagella and cilia of other organisms. The flagella of bacteria are very thin, consisting of a single fibril in cross section. Only a single kind of protein, a type of protein that belongs to the keratin-myosin group of contractile proteins of animals, occurs in bacterial flagella. The number and arrangement of the flagella on the cell are variable, and this information is used in bacterial identification.

The growth of a bacterial population in culture follows a predictable pattern. A typical S-shaped growth curve results when a culture is inoculated with bacteria, and the increase in cell numbers is plotted on a graph as a function of time (Fig. 2-9a). The growth curve can be divided into four parts: (I) lag phase, (II) logarithmic phase, (III) stationary phase, and (IV) senescent phase. The lag phase is a period of cell adjustment to the new medium, a period of protoplasmic synthesis, cell enlargement, and preparation for division. The length of the lag phase depends upon the prior history of the cells in the initial inoculum and the conditions under which the new culture is maintained.

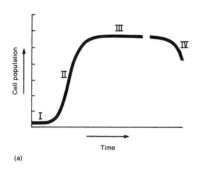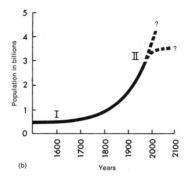

**Figure 2-9.** Growth curves. (a) Growth curve of a bacterial population. I. lag phase; II. logarithmic phase; III. stationary phase; and IV. senescent phase. (b) Growth curve of the human population of the world. I. lag phase and II. logarithmic phase.

The logarithmic (or exponential) phase is the period of active cell division. One cell gives rise to two, two to four, four to eight, and so on. The more cells there are, the more offspring following each division. Given a constant generation time and each cell capable of division, the cell population will increase at an exponential rate. The steepness of the slope depends on a number of factors, including the ability of each cell of the population to divide as rapidly as the other cells.

The stationary phase is the period in which there is no net increase in cell number. This means that the rate of cell division equals that of cell death. The cause for the slowdown in growth rate from the logarithmic phase to the stationary one is variable. The depletion from the medium of one or more specific nutrients required for growth is the cause in some cases; a buildup of toxic compounds in the medium is the cause in others.

Later, the stationary phase gives way to a stage in which there is a decline in the number of viable cells in the population. At this time the rate of cell death exceeds the rate of cell replenishment. This is the sign of a senescent culture, and the population will continue to die unless the medium is changed.

The S-shaped growth curve is of broad biological interest. It describes the growth characteristics of other unicellular organisms. In multicellular organisms, it describes the growth characteristics of organs that have determinant growth (such as the plant leaf). The S-shaped growth curve also describes the potential for population growth of multicellular organisms. The growth of the human population is of interest in this regard (Fig. 2-9b). Here, the world's population is seen to have entered the logarithmic phase of growth, and there is no present evidence to indicate that the rate of population increase is slowing. When will the stationary phase be reached? In other words, how large a population will the earth support on a continuing basis without some kind of

---

irreparable damage done to our essentially closed ecological system? Will we run out of living space, or will the population be limited by a buildup of toxic substances (pollutants?) in our environment, or by a depletion of needed compounds (food?)? Will man continue to use his irreplaceable natural resources and continue to pollute his environment at an ever increasing rate so that the stationary phase, when reached, will soon lead to a steady decline in population? Or, will man work to limit early his population size in order to live well within the limits imposed by our growth system, so that there is a comfortable margin of safety and so that the stationary phase can be extended indefinitely? These are some of the major unanswered questions that face mankind today — questions that must be answered if life, as we know it, is to continue on our planet.

Most bacteria have no special structures by which they survive periods unfavorable for vegetative growth. The cell itself is able to survive these conditions. However, a few bacteria develop spores within the cytoplasm; hence the spores are called *endospores*. The spores, resistant to elevated temperature, desiccation, and radiation, are released upon death and disintegration of the cell wall. Since a single spore develops per cell, the spores do not cause an increase in cell number in the population. They do have survival value. Many types of home-canned food spoilage are due to the survival during the canning process of spores of *Clostridium botulinum,* an anaerobic bacterium. Toxin formed by this bacterium (one of the most lethal poisons known) affects the nervous system and produces the type of food poisoning known as botulism.

### Modes of Nutrition

Depending on their nutritional capabilities, bacteria can be placed in two general classes: *autotrophs* and *heterotrophs*. Heterotrophic bacteria require for growth the presence of organic carbon compounds in the surrounding medium. They are unable to synthesize these compounds from carbon dioxide and thus cannot make their own food. Heterotrophic bacteria obtain carbon compounds either from dead organic matter (saprobic bacteria) or from living organisms (parasitic bacteria). Not all heterotrophic bacteria, however, can readily be classified as either saprobes or parasites. Many bacteria pathogenic to man can also be cultured on artificial media in the laboratory. Organisms that usually live as parasites, but that may also exist as saprobes, are called *facultative* parasites.

Autotrophic organisms synthesize organic carbon compounds from carbon dioxide; they make their own food. Energy to drive these synthetic reactions is obtained either in the form of radiant energy from the sun (*photoautotrophic* bacteria) or by the oxidation of inorganic compounds (*chemoautotrophic* bacteria). The nutritional types of bacteria are described in more detail below.

*Saprotism.* Saprobes form the largest nutritional group of bacteria, and they are of great economic importance to man. Along with fungal saprobes, they are responsible for the decay and recycling of organic matter in nature (Figs. 2-10; 2-12). The free-living, nitrogen-fixing bacteria are saprobic organisms. Saprobic bacteria are also responsible for considerable food spoilage and food poisoning.

Many saprobic bacteria, however, are of benefit to man. They are important in the production of cheeses, sauerkraut, organic acids such as lactic and acetic acids, and alcohols. The antibiotics Aureomycin, bacitracin, Chloromycetin, and streptomycin are other important products of saprobic bacteria.

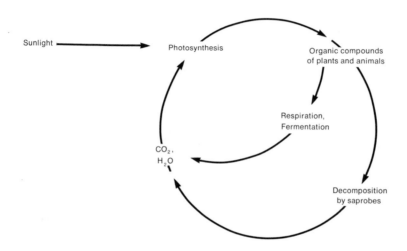

**Figure 2-10.** The carbon cycle.

*Parasitism.* Parasitism is a form of *symbiosis* in which one organism lives at the expense of the other. (Symbiosis is broadly defined as the living together in close association of two dissimilar organisms. Some people restrict the definition to include only those relationships in which there is mutual benefit.) Bacterial parasites obtain nutrients from the host and, at the same time, have a harmful effect on the host. The adverse effect is generally due to the enzymatic destruction of host tissue, or to the formation of toxins that either diffuse from living bacterial cells or are released upon death of these cells. Numerous pathogenic bacteria of man, animals, and plants are known. Well-known bacterial diseases of man include cholera, diphtheria, bacterial pneumonia, plague, scarlet fever, tuberculosis, and whooping cough.

*Photoautotrophism.* Photosynthetic bacteria are a relatively small group of organisms. They are anaerobic organisms and occur in a wide variety of aquatic environments. Three groups of photosynthetic bacteria are recognized: the green sulfur bacteria, the purple sulfur bacteria, and the purple nonsulfur bacteria. At least four different kinds of bacterial chlorophylls are known, none of which is identical to any chlorophyll of other organisms. Recent custom is to call them all bacteriochlorophylls and to identify each kind by a letter as a suffix. (For example, bacteriochlorophyll *a*, *b*, *c*, or *d*.) The purple color of many of these bacteria is due to the presence of carotenoid pigments.

Bacterial photosynthesis differs from that of algae and other plants in three general ways. First, water is not the hydrogen donor, as it is in algae and in other plants. Instead, bacteria utilize reduced hydrogen compounds such as hydrogen sulfide ($H_2S$) or organic compounds such as propionic acid. Second, molecular oxygen is not a byproduct of bacterial photosynthesis. For example, either elemental sulfur or the sulfate ion ($SO_4^=$) is the byproduct of photosynthetic bacteria that utilize hydrogen sulfide. Third, bacterial photosynthesis occurs only under anaerobic conditions. Other photosynthetic organisms normally require aerobic conditions. An over-all reaction for photosynthesis by green and purple sulfur bacteria is:

$$CO_2 + 2H_2S \xrightarrow[\substack{\text{light, anaerobic} \\ \text{conditions}}]{\substack{\text{bacterio-} \\ \text{chlorophyll}}} (CH_2O) + 2S + H_2O$$

Radiant energy from sunlight is converted to chemical energy in the form of carbohydrates ($CH_2O$). The necessary raw materials are carbon dioxide and a hydrogen donor such as hydrogen sulfide. The products of the reaction are carbohydrates, elemental sulfur (S), and water. The sulfur is usually first deposited intracellularly and is later converted to sulfate and given off to the environment.

The chlorophyll pigments, like those of other photosynthetic organisms, occur in membranes, but the membranes are not contained within chloroplasts. The pigments of bacteria are contained within structures called *photosynthetic membranes.* (These structures have also been called chromatophores, but the term chromatophore is also used to describe chloroplasts in the various groups of algae. Recent custom is *not* to use the term chromatophore to describe the bacterial photosynthetic system.) Studies have shown that, like the mesosomes, the photosynthetic membranes of at least some bacteria are continuous with, and arise by the invagination of, the cell membrane (Fig. 2-11). Photosynthetic bacteria are useful research organisms in the study of the photosynthetic process, which here is not as complex as it is in other plants. These bacteria are also of historical interest, because the first understanding of the over-all photosynthetic reaction was obtained as a result of studies on photosynthetic bacteria.

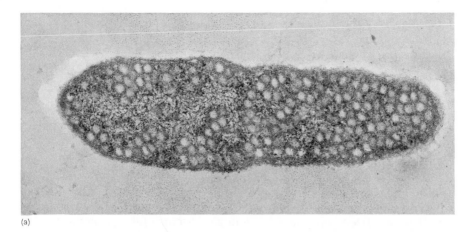

(a)

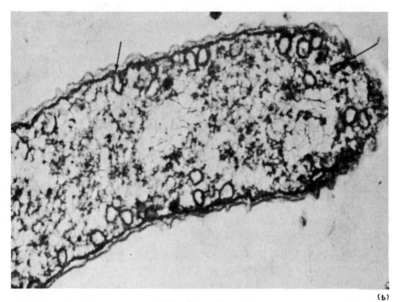

(b)

**Figure 2-11.** Electronmicrographs showing cellular organization of photosynthetic bacteria. (a) *Rhodopseudomonas spheroides* grown in a light intensity of 50 footcandles. The vesicular structures are photosynthetic membranes. Courtesy of Dr. G. Cohen-Bazire, University of California, Berkeley. (b) *Rhodospirillum rubrum.* Arrows indicate invaginated regions of the cell membrane. This cell had been previously treated with the enzyme ribonuclease—a treatment that makes the cellular membranes more visible. Compare with (a) above. Photo courtesy of Dr. G. Cohen-Bazire, from G. Cohen-Bazire and R. Kunisawa, *J. Cell Biol.,* 16:401–419 (1963).

*Chemoautotrophism.* Chemoautotrophic bacteria are a unique nutritional group of aerobic organisms that obtain carbon (necessary in the synthesis of organic carbon compounds) directly from carbon dioxide by means other than photosynthesis. The energy used to drive these synthetic reactions is obtained from the oxidation of inorganic molecules such as nitrogen, sulfur, and iron compounds. Two energy-yielding reactions are:

$$NH_4^+ + 2O_2 \longrightarrow 2H_2O + NO_2^- + Energy \quad (Nitrosomonas)$$

$$2NO_2^- + O_2 \longrightarrow 2NO_3^- + Energy \quad (Nitrobacter)$$

Once energy has been obtained, the synthesis of organic compounds occurs and is summarized:

$$CO_2 + H_2O + Energy \longrightarrow Organic\ compounds$$

*Nitrosomonas* and *Nitrobacter* are so-called nitrifying bacteria of the nitrogen cycle (described below). Other chemoautotrophic bacteria, known as iron bacteria, have been implicated in the origin of some of the economically important iron deposits, such as the Mesabi Range in Minnesota.

Heterotrophic and autotrophic bacteria are important because they participate in the recycling of organic matter. The involvement of bacteria in the nitrogen cycle is described here in detail because protein synthesis in all organisms depends on the availability of nitrogen compounds. The nitrogen cycle is diagrammed in Fig. 2-12. Many plants, including crop plants, obtain nitrogen rapidly from the soil only when it is in the form of the nitrate ion ($NO_3^-$). Large amounts of this ion are absorbed by plants from the soil, and the nitrogen is bound in plant proteins as an amino group ($-NH_2$). When eaten by animals, the nitrogen in plant proteins is incorporated into animal proteins. Upon the death of plants and animals, protein decomposition results in the formation and release into the soil of the ammonium ion ($NH_4^+$). Two types of aerobic bacteria, the so-called *nitrifying* bacteria, convert the ammonium ion back into the nitrate ion. One type (*Nitrosomonas*) converts ammonium to the nitrite ion ($NO_2^-$), and then the other type (*Nitrobacter*) converts nitrite to nitrate. This is the method whereby nitrates are made available to plants under natural conditions. The cycle is upset when plants are harvested and removed from the fields in which they grew. This agricultural procedure results in the continual depletion of nitrates (and other ions such as phosphates) from the soil; the nitrates must then be replaced by the periodic addition of fertilizers to the soil.

Soil nitrate is also reduced in amount by the metabolic activities of many different anaerobic bacteria, called *denitrifying* bacteria. By a series of chemical reactions (reductions), these denitrifying bacteria cause the nitrogen present in nitrates to be released to the atmosphere as nitrogen gas ($N_2$). Maintenance of aerobic conditions in fields, accomplished by proper soil drainage and tillage, tends to reduce the rate of denitrification.

Gaseous nitrogen is returned to the soil by a process called nitrogen fixation. Some of the nitrogen-fixing bacteria, such as the aerobic genus *Azotobac-*

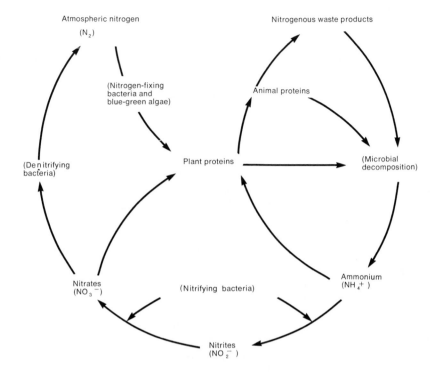

Atmospheric nitrogen
(N$_2$)

(Nitrogen-fixing
bacteria and
blue-green algae)

Nitrogenous waste products

Animal proteins

(Denitrifying
bacteria)

Plant proteins

(Microbial
decomposition)

Nitrates
(NO$_3{}^-$)

(Nitrifying bacteria)

Ammonium
(NH$_4{}^+$)

Nitrites
(NO$_2{}^-$)

**Figure 2-12.** The nitrogen cycle.

*ter* and the anaerobic genus *Clostridium,* are common, free-living, soil organisms. Others live in symbiotic relationship with roots of many leguminous plants such as beans, clover, vetch, and alfalfa. Both free-living bacteria and symbiotic bacteria, which are found in root *nodules,* incorporate gaseous nitrogen into bacterial amino acids and proteins. The process by which this is done is not well understood. Death of nitrogen-fixing bacteria makes the nitrogenous compounds in their cells available to other plants.

### Summary (Bacteria)

| Photosynthetic Pigments | Flagella | Food Reserve |
|---|---|---|
| Bacteriochlorophyll *a*<br>Bacteriochlorophyll *b*<br>Bacteriochlorophyll *c*<br>Bacteriochlorophyll *d* | Bacterial-type, single fibril in cross section. | Variable. |

*Additional:* prokaryotic cellular structure (no nuclear, mitochondrial, or chloroplast envelopes); primarily nonphotosynthetic and heterotrophic organisms; amitotic nuclear division; conjugation type of sexuality.

### Evolutionary Relationships (Bacteria)

Because of their prokaryotic cellular structure, simple forms, and tremendous nutritional diversity, bacteria are believed to represent a primitive group of organisms. This belief is supported by the geologic record. Fossil bacteria (or at least bacteria-like fossils) have been found in Precambrian strata (see Appendix for a geologic timetable), including rocks from South Africa dated about 3.2 billion years old. These Precambrian bacteria-like fossils have forms and sizes comparable to existing bacteria, although nothing is known about their cellular structures. Of interest is a living organism that is morphologically comparable to a Canadian middle Precambrian fossil (age about 2 billion years). The organism was not described until 1968, after the discovery of the Precambrian fossil (in 1965). It (the living organism) was isolated from a soil sample from Wales, and has a rather odd growth requirement. This apparently uncommon organism appears to be an obligate ammoniophile (philos = loving) and a facultative aerobe (see Siegel and Siegel, Selected Readings). Several huge iron ore deposits are further evidence for the existence of Precambrian bacteria; these ore deposits are believed to have resulted from the metabolic activities of chemoautotrophic bacteria.

In regard to cellular structure, bacteria appear to be more closely related to blue-green algae than to any other group of plants. (An evaluation of this relationship will be deferred until the blue-green algae have been discussed.)

# 3

## Fungi

Fungi, or Eumycota (eu = true; mykes = fungus), are eukaryotic organisms that lack chlorophyll. Being nonphotosynthetic, fungi depend on the products of other organisms, either living or dead, for food. Their ability to break down and utilize a wide variety of complex compounds accounts for their being able to live on a myriad of organic substrates. While fungi are ubiquitous as a group, the individual species usually are more limited in their nutritional tolerances. Fungi are of great economic importance. Some are parasites of animals and man. Many are virulent parasites of crop plants, resulting in considerable loss of food to man. Some fungi have by-products such as antibiotics and organic acids which man can use. Yeasts are indispensable to baking and brewing industries. Characteristic flavors of cheeses result from the presence of certain fungi; for example, Roquefort and Camembert cheeses are flavored (and colored) by the growths in the cheeses of *Penicillium roqueforti* and *P. camemberti*, respectively. A large industry is devoted to the culture of mushrooms for market. In addition, several fungi, such as morels and truffles, are highly prized by gourmets.

### Thallus Differentiation

The thallus of most fungi is differentiated into a vegetative portion and reproductive structures.

The nuclei of fungi are small (many are about three microns in diameter), and the electron microscope is used to elucidate details of nuclear division. Cells of fungi (like animal cells) either have centrioles or centriole-like bodies. Centrioles are small organelles that migrate to opposite poles of the nucleus prior to mitosis, and the mitotic spindle apparatus is organized between them. In some fungi, the nuclear envelope disappears late during mitosis, and the ends of the spindle fibers (as in animal cells) are in contact with the centrioles or centriole-like bodies. In other fungi, the nuclear envelope persists during the entire mitotic division, and the spindle is entirely intranuclear, separated from the centrioles by an intact nuclear envelope (Fig. 3-1).

In many fungi, the extensive vegetative part is not seen because it grows within and obtains nutrients from the substrate; only the reproductive structures are visible. Characteristically, the vegetative portion is either unicellular or filamentous. Fungal filaments, known as *hyphae* (hyphe = a web; singular: hypha), are usually highly branched, and together are known as the *mycelium* (from mykes = fungus; plural: mycelia) of the organism. Hyphal growth is by the widespread but poorly understood process known as tip growth. This process restricts cell wall synthesis and cell enlargement to the hyphal apex.

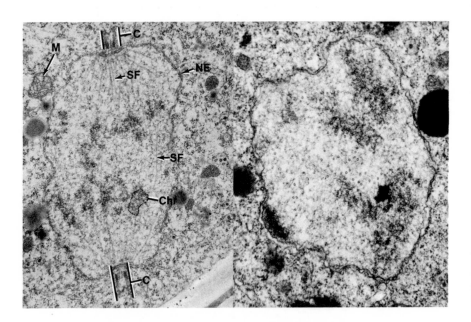

**Figure 3-1.**  Anaphase stage of mitosis in the fungus *Catenaria*. The nuclear envelope (NE) remains intact during nuclear division. Note also the centrioles (C) at each pole of the mitotic spindle, spindle fibers (SF), chromosomes (Chr), and mitochondria (M). Courtesy of Dr. M. S. Fuller, University of Georgia, Athens; from A. A. Ichida and M. S. Fuller, *Mycologia*, 60:141–155 (1968).

Protein synthesis, on the other hand, is not restricted to the tip. For example, a study of the distribution of protein synthesis in hyphae of *Neurospora* has shown that synthesis of protein occurs throughout the filament. Cytoplasmic streaming subsequently results in the movement of proteins to the actively growing hyphal tips.

As hyphae grow, they continually come in contact with new substrates. Since most organic substances are too large to pass directly through the cell wall and plasma membrane, there is a continuous secretion of enzymes into the substrate (these enzymes, therefore, are called *exoenzymes*). The enzymes break down the complex compounds into molecules small enough to enter the cell. Food not utilized immediately is stored as the carbohydrate glycogen or as droplets of oil.

The cell walls of fungi are chemically complex (see Bartnicki-Garcia, Suggestions for Further Readings). Chitin is widespread but is absent from some taxonomic groups (e.g., the Oomycetes). Cellulose, on the other hand, has a restricted distribution (it occurs, however, in the Oomycetes). The presence of either chitin or cellulose in the wall does not preclude the presence of the other compound; recently it has been confirmed that both polymers can occur together in the walls of some fungi.

Changes in the cell wall composition during fungal morphogenesis has been well documented in several fungi. One of the most detailed studies of this kind has been carried out on *Mucor rouxii,* an organism that exhibits filamentous (mold-like) growth under aerobic conditions and yeast-like (unicellular) growth under anaerobic conditions. A striking difference in wall thickness exists between these two growth forms; the yeast-like wall is about 10 times thicker than that of the filamentous wall. Correlated with this increased wall thickness is a distinctly higher mannose (a hexose sugar) and protein content. (The true budding yeasts, such as *Saccharomyces cereviseae,* also have cell walls with a high mannose content, whereas the cell walls of most filamentous fungi contain very little or no mannose.)

Detailed study of the external factors that control the transition from mold-like to yeast-like growth has shown that anaerobic conditions *per se* do not cause mold-yeast dimorphism in *Mucor rouxii.* Change in form occurs only when the carbon dioxide concentration is high; filamentous growth continues when the atmosphere is nitrogen. Furthermore, the effective morphogenetic agent is the physically dissolved $CO_2$, not the bicarbonate ion in solution. In *M. rouxii* it is thus possible experimentally to control morphogenesis by altering a single environmental factor.

How does carbon dioxide alter cellular metabolism? It is now known that organisms in general are capable of nonphotosynthetic incorporation of $CO_2$ into cellular constituents. In *Mucor rouxii* analysis showed that radioactive $CO_2$ was incorporated primarily into the aspartic acid component of the cell wall protein, a protein that is particularly rich in aspartic acid. Further study showed that the malic enzyme is involved in the fixation of $CO_2$ by pyruvate with the subsequent formation of aspartate. A simplified sequence of events is given below:

$$\text{Pyruvate} + CO_2 \xrightarrow[\text{enzyme}]{\text{malic}} \text{malate} \longrightarrow \text{aspartate} \longrightarrow \begin{array}{l}\text{incorporation}\\\text{into cell}\\\text{wall proteins}\end{array}$$

The evidence thus suggests that anaerobic conditions plus a high $CO_2$ tension shift the biosynthetic machinery of the cell toward increased $CO_2$ fixation, and this is followed by an increased mannan and protein content in the thickened cell wall.

The question of how aspartate or mannan-protein control the growth characteristics of *Mucor rouxii* is still unanswered. One working hypothesis is that increased synthesis of mannan- and protein-containing aspartate disrupts or prevents the establishment of gradients during the deposition of cell wall components. A gradient, in turn, is necessary for the maintenance of the tip growth characteristic of fungal hyphae. Verification of this awaits further investigation.

Similar correlations between changes in wall composition during morphogenesis have been found in other fungi, and this has led to the suggestion that, at least in fungi, the question of morphological development can be reduced to a question of cell wall biosynthesis. This notion again points up the extreme importance of the cell wall in plant biology. (The importance of the cell wall in maintaining cell shape was discussed in the section on bacteria, Chapter 2.)

The reproductive structures of fungi are remarkable for their diversity of form, and identification of species of fungi is based largely on features of the reproductive structures. Spore formation is the most common method of reproduction in fungi. *Spore* is a general term used to describe nearly all detachable asexual reproductive units of the fungus, except unmodified hyphal fragments. Spores are small, usually unicellular bodies that, upon germination, give rise to a new plant. There are many different kinds of spores, and a single fungus may form more than one type during its development. An elaborate terminology has developed to describe the various types of fungal spores (e.g., sporangiospores, zoospores, conidia, aeciospores, teliospores, oidia, chlamydospores, and blastospores, to name a few). The terminology is often overwhelming for the elementary student, and since much of this terminology can be introduced when needed in advanced courses, many of these terms will not be used in this book. Most of the variety of spores formed by fungi (as well as by other plants) simply will be referred to as *mitospores* and *meiospores*. (These terms were originally used by Professor Ralph Emerson, University of California, Berkeley, to refer specifically to types of spores formed by the fungus *Allomyces* [see later]. Because of their usefulness the terms are used in a broader sense in this volume.) Since some teachers will prefer to continue use of the specific spore name, it will usually be given in parenthesis where appropriate and the interested student can use the term immediately.

*Mitospores* are spores formed during asexual reproduction and are so-named because they develop following mitotic divisions. Therefore mitospores may be haploid or diploid depending on the ploidy of the parent. *Conidia* and *sporangiospores* are two common kinds of mitospores. Conidia (konis = dust) are produced singly or in chains from the tips of either hyphae or modified hyphal branches called *conidiophores*. Conidia are not flagellated. Sporangiospores develop in sac-like structures called *sporangia* (sporos = a seed; angeion = receptacle). The sporangiospores of many fungi are flagellated—in which case they are called zoospores (zoion = animal). Mitospore formation generally begins soon after the organism becomes established on the substrate, and spores are developed continuously or in successive waves as long as environmental conditions (such as an adequate food supply) are favorable. Many types of mitospores are thin-walled and are capable of immediate germination on a suitable substrate. Mitospore production results in a rapid buildup of fungal populations in a nutritionally favorable area, and in the spread of the fungus to new regions. This asexual cycle is referred to as the *repeating cycle,* because several generations of mitospores may be produced during a growing season.

*Meiospores* are formed following meiosis and thus are haploid. Formation of these spores is discussed in more detail later. They may be flagellated (and called zoospores) or nonflagellated. Meiospore function is similar to that of mitospores in that they aid in the dispersal of the fungus to new substrates. Moreover, since they develop after meiosis, meiospores may carry new gene combinations that make the fungus better adapted to its substrate or to a changing environment.

A third type of spore is formed by many fungi. These spores, oospores and zygospores, develop following sexual reproduction and are diploid. In such fungi, the zygote does not directly undergo meiosis to give rise to meiospores; nor does it germinate to give rise to a diploid plant. Instead, the zygote becomes thick-walled and undergoes a period of dormancy. The induction of sexual reproduction, which leads to the formation of these dormant structures, generally occurs near the end of the vegetative growing period of the fungus, when the available food supply in the substrate becomes diminished. Many of the spores are unable to germinate until after an obligate period of dormancy, and they are able to survive harsh environmental conditions. Thus these spores have the primary function of enabling the organism to survive periods unfavorable to vegetative growth.

In general we know much more about the nutritional requirements for supporting vegetative growth than we do about the environmental factors that stimulate asexual and sexual reproduction. Even less is known about the biochemical process involved in the induction of the reproductive structures.

## Classification

The scheme of classification of fungi to be used in this book is the one suggested by Alexopoulos (see Suggestions for Further Reading). He recognizes eight more or less natural classes, of which only five will be discussed here: Chytridiomycetes, Oomycetes, Zygomycetes, Ascomycetes, and Basidiomycetes. Separation of classes is based mainly on details of sexual reproduction and form of flagellated cells (Fig. 3-2), when present.

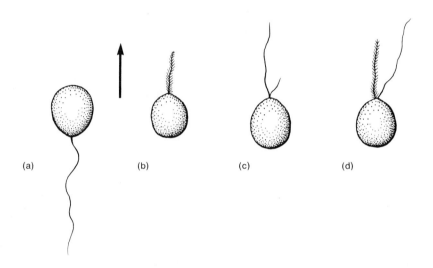

(a)        (b)        (c)        (d)

**Figure 3-2.** Types of flagellar arrangement in fungi. (a) Chytridiomycetes with a single posterior whiplash flagellum. (b) Hyphochytridiomycetes with a single anterior tinsel flagellum. (c) Plasmodiophoromycetes with two anterior whiplash flagella of unequal lengths. (d) Oomycetes with two flagella, one whiplash and one tinsel. Examples of (b) and (c) are not discussed in this book. Flagellated cells are lacking in the Zygomycetes, Ascomycetes, and Basidiomycetes.

In another, older classification in general use, the Chytridiomycetes, Oomycetes, and Zygomycetes are all placed in a single class, the Phycomycetes (phyco = seaweed). The Phycomycetes, in turn, are those fungi that have a relatively simple, non-septate, and multinucleate (coenocytic) thallus. These fungi have similar thallic structure, but I feel that lumping them together in a single class tends to obscure very important differences.

There are, however, many fungi in which sexual reproduction has never been found, and it is therefore impossible to place them with certainty in any of the groups above. These fungi either have lost their ability to form sexual structures or have not yet been cultured under the proper conditions to induce sexual reproduction. It is possible, too, that sexual reproduction has not been recognized. These fungi are lumped together in a class called the Deuteromycetes (deutero = secondary), or Fungi Imperfecti. (The sexual stage is considered to be the perfect stage.) Thus constituted, the Fungi Imperfecti is an artificial grouping of organisms which resemble each other primarily in that they lack sexual reproduction. Therefore this taxon does not enjoy the same taxonomic meaning as the five groups above. Most of man's skin diseases, such as ringworm and athlete's foot, and a few of his respiratory and other diseases are caused by these imperfect fungi. There are also large numbers of plant diseases caused by the Fungi Imperfecti. Identification of imperfect fungi depends primarily on details of asexual reproductive structures. Although many of these fungi have asexual reproductive structures similar to those of Ascomycetes, we cannot be sure that they are, in fact, Ascomycetes, until sexual structures are found.

After a discussion of the modes of fungal nutrition, the specific characteristics of the five groups mentioned above will be considered.

**Modes of Nutrition**

The nutritional requirements of fungi are the same as those of other plants, but fungi are *heterotrophs* (heteros = other; trophe = nourishment) since they cannot synthesize their own food. No *autotrophic* (autos = self) fungi are known (while there *are* autotrophic bacteria). For energy sources, fungi utilize various organic carbon compounds, often simple sugars. The amount of nutrients present is not the only factor in determining whether a fungus will grow on a particular substance. The chemical nature of the substrate and its availability to the fungus also are important. Fungi that thrive in slightly acid media may be completely inhibited on neutral or slightly basic substances. The reverse may be true for other fungi. This knowledge has been used to control the growth of some fungi. Fungi generally require the presence in the medium of one or more complex organic growth factors (such as vitamins) for growth. Absence of these factors inhibits growth, even though sufficient available organic carbon compounds are present.

Fungi do more than merely absorb food; they also affect the physical and chemical nature of the substrate on which they grow. In some instances, such as in brewer's yeast, they modify their environment so that they can no longer grow, even though nutrients are still available. During respiration, brewer's yeast metabolizes sugars and gives off ethyl alcohol into the medium as a by-product. The concentration of alcohol increases to a level (around 15 per cent) that is inhibitory to the further growth of the yeast.

Fungi have long been divided into two major groups—saprobes (also referred to as saprophytes: sapros = rotten; phyton = plant) and parasites—depending on their mode of nutrition. Not all fungi readily fit in either of the two categories. Although most fungi are either strict saprobes or obligate parasites (having an absolute requirement for a living host), there are some that can grow on both living and dead material. These fungi are known as facultative parasites or facultative saprobes. Moreover, there is an additional type of symbiotic relationship found in fungi. Some fungi form associations with other plants, vascular and nonvascular, in which both partners benefit. This symbiotic relationship is termed mutualism.

### Saprotism

Fungal saprobes, along with bacterial saprobes, are scavengers of the plant kingdom. They utilize numerous organic compounds, from simple sugars to complex organic carbon substances, making energy tied up in these compounds available for growth and development. Saprobes have a considerable influence on our daily lives. Many are important agents of food spoilage. Molds on bread, jelly, jam, and syrup are familiar examples of saprotism, although not as common as they used to be because of the addition of various growth retardants to foodstuffs. Other saprobes are important in food processing, such as baking and cheese-making, and in the production of organic acids and alcohols. Wherever humidity is high, saprobes are particularly troublesome, because they rapidly degrade leather, paper, textiles, and even insulation on electrical appliances.

Saprobic fungi also are of considerable importance to foresters and lumbermen. Fungi cause extensive damage to our forest trees. A large number of wood-decomposing fungi, mostly Basidiomycetes, are known. Many of them decompose wood of living trees. In many cases, the vegetative mycelium completely decomposes the inside of trees before there is any external evidence of fungal infection. These fungi normally live in the dead cells of the trees and their hydrolytic enzymes break down the cellulose and hemicellulose of the cell walls. The sugars released then enter the metabolic pathways that furnish the fungal cells with energy and building blocks. Some wood-decomposing fungi primarily attack carbohydrates of the middle lamella and primary wall, others attack carbohydrates of the secondary wall, and still others break down lignin. The infected trees are worthless to the lumber industry. Moreover, infected trees occupy valuable space in the forests and serve as reservoirs for the spread of the fungus to other trees.

### Parasitism

Parasitic fungi have plagued man ever since he changed from a nomadic to an agricultural existence. Practically all plants of use to man have one or more fungal parasites. As in the cases of bacterial diseases, fungi may be pathogenic and quickly kill the host, or they may have a balanced relationship in which they obtain nutrients from the plant without killing it. Plant parasites have representatives in all fungal groups.

There are three general ways in which a fungal parasite grows in and obtains nutrients from its host. In some of the simpler, unicellular fungi, an individual derived from a single spore will enter and infect only one cell of the host. Its whole development is confined to this single host cell. Parasites of this type are common on algae, other fungi, and roots of flowering plants. The degree of infection depends on the number of spores in the surrounding medium. Many of these fungi are host specific, and there is evidence to indicate that the host exudes specific substances into the medium that attract the motile spores of the fungus.

Most parasitic fungi are filamentous, and their growth is not restricted to the confines of a single host cell. In many of these, hyphae predominantly grow between the cells of the host in the region of the middle lamella, and hence are termed intercellular hyphae. Specialized lateral filaments, called *haustoria*, penetrate cells adjacent to these intercellular hyphae and function as nutrient-absorbing structures (Fig. 3-3). They contain a large number of mitochondria, in addition to nuclei. Haustoria do not actually penetrate the protoplast of the host cell, but merely invaginate the cell membrane. This greatly increases the absorptive surface that the fungus has in contact with the host protoplast. Fungi that absorb nutrients over long periods of time without killing the host usually possess this kind of hyphal differentiation. In other mycelial parasites, hyphae grow through cell lumens as well as cell walls, often causing complete tissue destruction. Many of these are extremely destructive plant parasites.

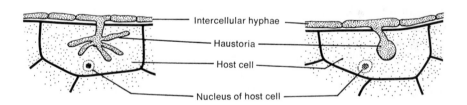

Intercellular hyphae

Haustoria

Host cell

Nucleus of host cell

**Figure 3-3.** Diagrammatic representation of two forms of fungal haustoria.

The seriousness of infection caused by any particular parasite depends on a combination of factors, including temperature, humidity, methods of crop cultivation, and kinds of control procedures used. A few parasitic fungi are of historical interest because they affected the economies and development of whole nations. Of considerable importance is *Phytophthora infestans* (phytophthora literally means "plant devourer"), an Oomycete that causes the disease called "late blight of potatoes." Just as our economy is based on the cereal grain, the Irish economy was based on the potato. The great Irish famine, beginning in 1845, was brought about through the destruction of the potato crop by this fungus. Over a million people died as a result of the famine, and more than that number emigrated to different lands, principally the United States and Canada. This fungus is still an ever-present danger in Ireland as well as in other potato-growing areas, but means are available to control the disease.

Another Oomycete, *Plasmopara viticola*, which causes downy mildew of grapes, nearly ruined the French wine industry during the 1870s and 1880s. It lives on the leaves, stems, and fruits of the grape plant, obtaining nutrients from host cells by means of haustoria. Originating in North America, where the native grapes are relatively unaffected by it, *Plasmopara viticola* was accidentally introduced into Europe. There the cultivated grapes were highly susceptible, and they sustained considerable damage. The mildew was not controlled until 1885, when a fungicide known as Bordeaux mixture (a dilute solution of copper sulfate and lime) came into use. This was the first commercial use of a fungicide, and it is still in use today.

Most parasitic fungi, however, have not been so drastic in their effect as the two discussed above. Nonetheless, all are ever-present problems. The field of plant pathology includes the study of the biology of fungal parasites. There are plant pathology departments in most large universities, and state and federal governments support research of many plant pathologists in field stations and other installations. Although their primary objective is to prevent and control plant diseases, plant pathologists also engage in research of a more fundamental nature.

Besides the plant parasites, there are many fungi that parasitize man, producing diseases generally termed *mycoses*. Often erroneously considered to be mainly tropical diseases, mycoses are common in the temperate climates as well. Many of them produce unsightly lesions of the skin, and some may result in death. Several types of "ringworm" are among the more familiar mycoses in the United States. In many cases, effective and specific control treatments are unknown. There are relatively few effective fungitoxic agents, in contrast to the many antibiotics available against parasitic bacteria. This is an active area of research.

Insects also have fungal parasites. One fungus lives on the common housefly in the more humid parts of the United States. Upon entry, the fungal mycelium grows throughout the body of the fly; just before the fly's death, which occurs within a week, the fly attaches itself firmly by its proboscis to a surface such as a windowpane. Shortly thereafter, asexual reproductive structures of the fungus emerge from the insect's body and spore discharge ensues. Attempts to use fungal parasites for biological control of insects have generally been unsuccessful.

A few parasitic fungi are remarkable in that they trap their prey, which may be amoebae, rhizopods, or nematodes (eel worms), by either adhesive or mechanical means. Adhesive traps may consist of hyphal branches, spherical knobs at the tips of short hyphae (which have been referred to as lethal lolli-pops), or hyphal rings or loops. The surfaces of many of these traps are coated with an adhesive substance to which the prey stick on contact. Certainly one of the most complex traps, a mechanical one, is produced by *Dactylella*. It is shaped like a noose and is triggered when a straying nematode attempts to move through it. On stimulation, cells of the noose swell considerably, trapping the nematode (Fig. 3-4). Subsequently, fungal filaments grow into and absorb nutrients from the nematode.

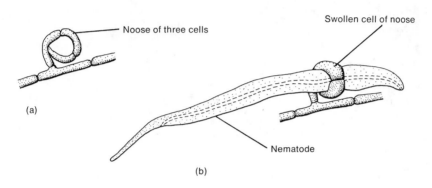

**Figure 3-4.**    Traps of the predaceous fungus *Dactylella*. (a) Open. (b) Swollen.

Predaceous fungi are not necessarily obligate predators. They are isolated from the soil with ease and grow without the presence of nematodes on a variety of complex organic media in axenic culture. Studies on *Arthrobotrys conoides* have shown that this fungus seldom forms traps when grown in axenic culture. However, traps readily form when nematodes, or water in which nematodes have been growing, or tissue extracts of nematodes, are added to the fungus culture. Thus we have a situation where the prey itself induces morphological change in the predator—a change necessary for the prey-predator relationship. There is evidence that the specific morphogenetic agent is of low molecular weight and that it is probably a peptide or an amino acid. Future research should identify this agent and clarify its involvement in the biochemistry of form development.

**Mutualism**

Mutualistic associations involving fungi and other plants are of considerable biological interest. In the preceding section we saw that many fungi obtain nutrients from living hosts. It may be somewhat surprising to find that some

---

(a)

**Figure 3-5.** Types of lichen thalli. (a) Foliose: *Parmelia centrifuga.* (b) Fructicose: *Cladonia alpestris.* (c) Crustose: *Ochrolechia frigida.* Courtesy of Dr. J. Langenheim, University of California, Santa Cruz.

fungi are also of benefit to their symbiont. Recent experimental studies have been directed toward the elucidation of the nature of this fungal benefit. Two types of mutualistic relationships will be described, *mycorrhizae* (associations of fungi and roots of vascular plants) and *lichens* (associations of fungi and algae).

*Mycorrhizae.* The mycorrhizal (mykes = fungus; rhiza = root) state is world-wide in distribution and has been found in the majority of seed-bearing plants studied. One investigator has even reported that it is present in all woody plants studied so far. Many different fungi are capable of establishing a mycorrhizal association, and, in some cases, different species of fungi can form mycorrhizae with a single species of seed-plant. Many of these are common soil fungi that apparently live as saprobes; the establishment of the association probably occurs whenever a root tip comes in contact with a receptive fungus. Two distinctive types of root-fungus relationships are found. In one type, the fungal mycelium forms a mantle on the surface of the root; only a few intercellular hyphae penetrate the root itself. In the second type, most of the hyphae live intracellularly within the root.

(b)

(c)

Even though mycorrhizae are of widespread occurrence, the nature of the interaction between fungal and nonfungal symbionts is not completely clear. Various theories have been proposed to explain this relationship. There is little doubt that in most cases fungi obtain organic compounds from nonfungal members. This has led to the suggestion that their relationship is essentially one of parasitism. Perhaps in some instances, especially those in which the fungus lives primarily within root tissue, this might be true. However, there is considerable evidence to indicate that in most cases these associations are beneficial to vascular plants. Most of this evidence comes from studies on conifers such as the pine. Cases have been reported in which trees with mycorrhizae grow better than those without. It has also been shown that mycorrhizal trees accumulate more inorganic salts than those without. Furthermore, in experiments utilizing radioactive tracer compounds, it has been shown that compounds absorbed by fungal hyphae can be transferred to the associated root. In these instances, the fungus apparently benefits its symbiont by increasing mineral salt absorption. It has also been suggested that fungi provide growth-promoting substances to the seed plant. Of course, further experimental work is necessary before any broad generalizations can be formulated to explain the beneficial effects of mycorrhizae.

*Lichens.* A lichen is a composite structure, consisting of an association between an alga and a fungus. Lichens are widespread, being found in arid and arctic regions as well as in temperate and tropical regions. They commonly grow on bare soil, trunks and branches of trees, fence posts, unweathered granitic rock, and other exposed places. Some marine lichens are known, but very little is known about them. Lichens can be white, black, or various shades of red, orange, yellow, or green. Some green lichens are readily confused with bryophytes, especially liverworts. Their coloration is due to the accumulation in the thallus of various (nonphotosynthetic) pigments, which are often different lichenic acids.

Some lichens have economic importance. Arctic reindeer and caribou feed on extensive patches of reindeer moss, which is a lichen. (Man, however, has apparently eaten lichens for food only in emergencies.) Prior to the discovery of coal tars, lichens were a major source of dyestuffs. Some still have commercial importance. For example, the well-known Harris Tweeds of Scotland are still dyed with native lichens. Lichens are also the source of the dye used in the preparation of litmus paper for chemistry. This dye turns blue in basic solutions and red in acid solutions. Further, some perfumes are still made from lichens. Of more recent interest is the discovery that some lichens produce substances that act as antibiotics against some fungi and some gram-positive bacteria not affected by the common antibiotics.

The form of the lichen thallus is variable (Fig. 3-5) and its internal structure may be relatively complex. While the thalli of a few lichens, especially those that contain a member of the Fungi Imperfecti, are polymorphic, others have distinctive shapes. It is the fungal member that is dominant and that determines the shape of the lichen thallus. In most lichens, the algae are restricted to a definite layer sandwiched between a compact upper fungal layer and a loose, spongy fungal layer below. In some lichens, an additional compact fungal layer is present on the lower surface of the thallus (Fig. 3-6).

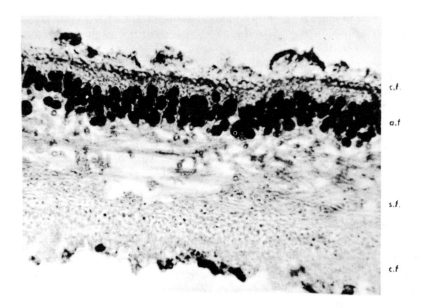

**Figure 3-6.** Section of a lichen. The darkly stained bodies are algal cells. Note compact fungal zone (c.f.), algal and fungal zone (a.f.), and spongy fungal zone (s.f.).

Lichens grow very slowly and generally have great longevity. In fact, as indicated earlier, they are often found in places not conducive to rapid growth. The ages of some of the arctic-alpine lichens have been estimated to range from 100 to 450 years. (Most lichens, however, are not so enduring.) Lichens can withstand alternate wetting and drying with no ill effect. Water absorption is very rapid (they can absorb up to 35 times their own weight in water) and loss of water is equally rapid. Lichens are also quite efficient accumulators of inorganic compounds. Presumably, this nutrient reservoir can be drawn upon at a later time. Their accumulation appears to be nonselective, and the accumulation of radioactive compounds (such as radioactive strontium) from nuclear explosion fallout has been documented. Since the lichen has no way to get rid of these compounds, and the thallus has great longevity, the concentrations continually increase. The long-term effect of this accumulation on the biology of the lichen, as well as on the animals that feed on lichens, remains to be assessed.

The algal component of lichens is either a green or a blue-green alga. The fungal element usually is an Ascomycete, but a few are Basidiomycetes or Fungi Imperfecti. Interestingly, the lichen fungi do not appear to live outside of the lichen in natural conditions, although they are readily grown in culture. On the other hand, the algal component does exist free of the lichen association.

Although they are composite structures, lichens are given binomial names as other organisms are. However, the name, which is based on fungal reproductive structures, belongs to the fungal component; the algae of lichens are similar to already-named, free-living algal species. The implication that each lichen possesses a different fungus needs experimental verification.

The nature of the relationship between algae and fungi in lichens is not fully explained. Some scientists suggest that the association is essentially a parasitic one, of balanced parasitism. They note that in many lichens the fungi are tightly appressed to—or, actually penetrate—the algal cells. There is little doubt that fungi obtain organic compounds from the algae. However, lichens are extremely stable and have extended longevity under natural conditions. That this relationship is more than simple parasitism is indicated by evidence suggesting that mineral ions absorbed by fungi may be made available to algae, and that fungi may exchange metabolites with the algae. However, there is no experimental evidence to support the commonly held belief that the fungi protect the algae against desiccation. Unfortunately, critical work has been done on very few lichens.

### Chytridiomycetes

Fungi placed in the Chytridiomycetes have reproductive cells with a single, posterior, whiplash flagellum (Fig. 3-2a). The vegetative bodies of some are unicellular and may lack a cell wall during certain stages of development. Depending on environmental conditions, the entire cell is converted into either a *sporangium* (a spore-producing structure) or a *gametangium* (a gamete-producing structure). Other Chytridiomycetes (such as *Allomyces*) are filamentous, and reproductive structures develop on their hyphal branches. Only the general form and development of *Allomyces* will be discussed here.

Species of *Allomyces* are aquatic organisms, common in (but not restricted to) warmer regions such as the tropics. They are plant and animal saprobes and often can be "captured" on boiled hemp or sesame seeds (or other suitable substrates) by covering dried soil with water and after the soil has settled, adding a few seeds for bait. If *Allomyces* is present in the soil, white hyphae will grow from the seed in a few days. Closer examination of the hyphae shows that the mycelium is differentiated into rhizoidal filaments that penetrate the substrate and absorb nutrients, and filaments that extend away from the substrate and bear gametangia (Fig. 3-7a). Male and female gametangia are borne on the same filament and, in some species, have a consistent spatial relationship to each other. The male gametangium is colored orange due to the presence of carotenoid pigments in the male gametes. The female gametes are colorless.

The presence of both male and female gametangia on the same filament, often in adjacent cells, indicates that sex expression in *Allomyces* is probably not under direct gene control, but is under extranuclear or cytoplasmic control. What are the biochemical mechanisms involved in sex expression and determination in organisms? Little is known about this basic problem. In *Allomyces* it has been suggested that carotenes (found here only in the male gametangium) might be the cause of sex differences. But it is more probable that carotene synthesis is the result, not the cause, of sex differences. More recent investigations show that female gametes have more RNA than male gametes have and that it is possible to alter the sex ratio in favor of male gametangia by experimentally interfering with RNA synthesis. Perhaps future research will indicate how RNA is involved in sex expression.

Gamete formation occurs by cleavage of the multinucleate cytoplasm into uninucleate male or female gametes in their respective gametangia. Mature gametes are discharged through one or more pores that develop in the gametangium wall (Fig. 3-7b, c). The male gamete, smaller and more actively motile than the female, is attracted to the female gamete, which secretes a hormone called *sirenin*. Sirenin has been purified, and its molecular structure has been completely worked out. Its mode of action on the male gamete has not yet been determined.

Fusion of gametes results in the formation of a zygote, which is propelled for a short time by two flagella, one contributed by each gamete. The zygote settles down on a suitable substrate, loses its flagella, and germinates into a new mycelium. The diploid mycelium is nearly identical in form to the haploid plant; thus *Allomyces* is said to have an "alternation of isomorphic generations." However, the reproductive structures on the diploid plant have quite different functions from those on the haploid. Two kinds of reproductive organs develop, *mitosporangia* and *meiosporangia*. Mitosporangia (Fig. 3-7e) are thin-walled and colorless, and they give rise to uniflagellate, diploid mitospores. Mitospore production results in a rapid population buildup in a short time period.

Meiosporangia (Fig. 3-7e) have brownish cell walls and are resistant structures. They enable *Allomyces* to survive conditions unfavorable for

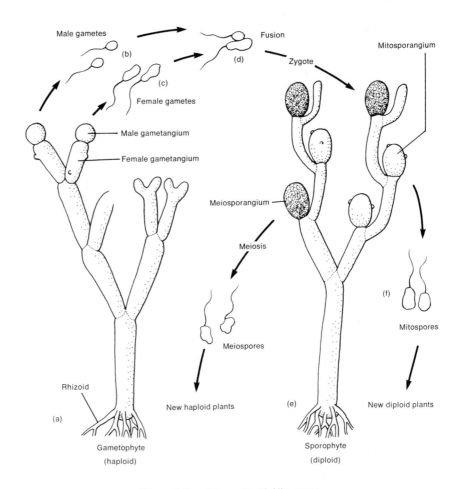

**Figure 3-7.** Life cycle of *Allomyces*.

vegetative growth—for example, when a pond in which it is growing dries up. These are the structures that would be present in the dry-soil samples mentioned above. When conditions are favorable for growth (such as when dry soil is placed in water), each nucleus in the resistant sporangium (there are usually

12) undergoes meiosis to form four haploid meiospores. The meiospores, each with a single, posterior, whiplash flagellum, emerge from the ruptured sporangium and swim around until they come in contact with a suitable substrate. Being haploid, meiospores give rise to haploid, gamete-producing plants. This explains why gamete-producing plants (gametophytes) are the first plants to appear in a new *Allomyces* culture, whereas the spore-producing plants (sporophytes) do not appear until later.

### Oomycetes

In contrast to fungi in the previous group, the flagellated mitospores (zoospores) of Oomycetes (oion = egg) each have one whiplash and one tinsel flagellum (Fig. 3-2d). Gametangia are of two morphologically dissimilar types: the male organ, called an *antheridium,* and the female organ, or *oogonium.* In most cases, gametangia are produced on specialized hyphal branches. In a few instances, the entire thallus (which in this case is unicellular) is converted into a gametangium.

Several Oomycetes are of considerable economic importance; some are among the most destructive parasites known. *Phytophthora infestans,* the cause of late blight of potato, and *Plasmopara viticola,* the cause of downy mildew of grapes, have already been discussed. *Saprolegnia* will be used as an example of this fungal class.

### Saprolegnia

Species of *Saprolegnia* are among the most common of the freshwater molds. Although a few are parasitic — on fish, for example — most are saprobes of dead animals. A common method to obtain *Saprolegnia* for study is to add an autoclaved fly to water that contains a small amount of soil. If *Saprolegnia* (or *Achlya,* a relative) is present, the fly will become surrounded by a halo of hyphae in a few days. The hyphae remain in the vegetative condition as long as abundant food is available.

Diminution of nutrients is assumed to result first in the formation of mitosporangia (zoosporangia) and later in the development of gametangia and oospores. The general sequence from vegetative hyphae to asexual reproduction to sexual reproduction, depending on nutrient conditions, has been known since the early part of the twentieth century. Very little has since been done to elucidate either factors that control these growth phases, or metabolic changes that occur within the mycelium as a result of these changes.

The nonseptate, vegetative hyphae of *Saprolegnia* are rather coarse and tubular. At the onset of asexual reproduction, hyphal tips become filled with cytoplasm and are cut off by crosswalls from the rest of the hyphae. These terminal cells become differentiated into mitosporangia (zoosporangia), and the flagellated mitospores (zoospores) are formed by the cleavage of the multinucleate cytoplasm within the sporangia (Fig. 3-8a). Mature mitospores (usually called primary mitospores, or primary zoospores) are discharged through an apical pore. They differ from those of *Allomyces* in that they possess two anterior flagella, one whiplash and one tinsel. After a period of motility, mitospores lose their flagella and encyst. Upon germination, each cyst gives rise to a single biflagellated mitospore, which is now called a secondary mitospore (or zoospore), in which the flagella are laterally inserted (Fig. 3-8b–d). Mitospores function to produce new plants on new nutrient sources.

In *Achlya* the discharged primary mitospores (zoospores) immediately encyst at the sporangial apex. The presence of this globular mass of encysted zoospores readily distinguishes *Achlya* from *Saprolegnia*. Subsequently, secondary mitospores (zoospores) are released.

As available nutrients continue to decrease, a further change in hyphal metabolism results in the development of sexual reproductive structures. Species of *Saprolegnia* are *hermaphroditic* (male and female sex organs are on a single plant) and *homothallic* (sexual structures on a single thallus are self-compatible). Male and female gametangia are highly specialized in form and function (Fig. 3-8e). The male structure or antheridium (anther = flower; -idium = a diminutive ending) produces sperm nuclei; the female gametangium or oogonium (oion = egg; gonos = offspring) produces eggs. During sexual reproduction, a hyphal branch, which produces the antheridium, grows toward

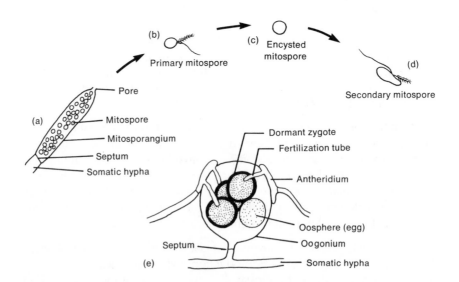

**Figure 3-8.** *Saprolegnia.* (a–d) Stages in asexual reproduction. (e) Sexual reproduction.

and comes in contact with the developing oogonium. (The interaction of hormones during sexual reproduction has been demonstrated in a related fungus, *Achlya ambisexualis,* by Dr. John Raper — see Suggestions for Further Reading.) Fertilization tubes, through which sperm nuclei pass, grow into the oogonium and come in contact with the eggs.

The diploid zygote produced by fusion of gamete nuclei develops a thick wall about itself and becomes a dormant structure called an *oospore.* Produced at a time when the nutrient supply is diminishing, the oospore functions to tide the organism over periods adverse for vegetative growth.

You will note that no attempt to identify haploid and diploid structures was made in the above account. Fusion of the sperm nucleus with the egg nucleus establishes the diploid phase. On the other hand, the time of meiosis has not been determined with certainty. For many years meiosis has been considered to occur during oospore germination, and the mycelium thus is haploid. However, recent studies on *Pythium debaryanum,* a relative of *Saprolegnia,* indicate that meiosis occurs in the antheridium during sperm formation and in the oogonium during egg development. Thus the possibility exists that the vegetative hyphae of *Saprolegnia* are diploid, and only the gametes are haploid. The place of meiosis needs confirmation. The small size of fungi nuclei (usually 2 to 3 $\mu$), and the fact that mitosis in many fungi occurs within the nuclear envelope, make interpretation of cytological studies difficult. Meiosis, on the other hand, differs in no essential respect from that in other plant groups.

### Zygomycetes

The Zygomycetes (zygon = yoke) include the black bread molds, several insect parasites, and a few predaceous fungi. These are all terrestrial fungi, and completely lack flagellated cells. The thallus is filamentous and, like the thalli of the preceding two classes, is generally nonseptate except in association with the reproductive structures. Asexual reproduction is by means of nonflagellated mitospores. Sexual reproduction involves the fusion of multinucleate gametangia. The resultant fusion cell is referred to as a *coenozygote,* rather than a zygote, because it contains more than one nucleus from each parent. The coenozygote then develops into a dormant zygospore.

The multinucleate, nonseptate thallus, formation of nonflagellated reproductive cells, and development of zygospores are the definitive features of this class of fungi. Two examples of the class are described below.

#### Rhizopus

*Rhizopus stolonifer (Rhizopus nigricans),* the black bread mold, is the species of *Rhizopus* most commonly studied in elementary courses. In con-

---

**Fungi**                                                                                                         **49**

trast to *Allomyces* and *Saprolegnia,* which grow in water, *Rhizopus stolonifer* is specialized for life on land. The non-septate, multinucleate mycelium of this species is differentiated into hyphae of three functional types (Fig. 3-9a). One type of hypha, called a *stolon,* rapidly grows over the surface of the substrate. *Rhizoids* arise at certain places along the stolon, and they grow into and break down the organic material of the substrate. A third type of hyphal branch, the *sporangiophore* (-phore = bearer), arises opposite the rhizoids, grows into the air, and gives rise to a terminal sporangium. The tip of the young sporangiophore is multinucleate, and the nuclei are arranged predominately in the peripheral cytoplasm. A curved wall that separates the spore-forming part of the cytoplasm from the vacuolate *columella* (diminutive of columen = column) then develops (Fig. 3-9b).

Wind-disseminated mitospores (sporangiospores) develop within the sporangium. The mitospores are small, dark-colored, and light in weight, and may remain suspended in the air for considerable periods of time. Sporangiophores aid spore dispersal in that they elevate the sporangium above the level of the substrate.

*Rhizopus stolonifer* is heterothallic but, because gametangia of the two sexes are morphologically similar, it is not possible to identify male and female plants. Therefore one strain is referred to as the plus strain and the other as the minus strain. So long as the strains are grown in separate cultures, no sexual reproductive structures are formed. When both strains are cultured together and the plus and minus hyphae are in close proximity to each other, short

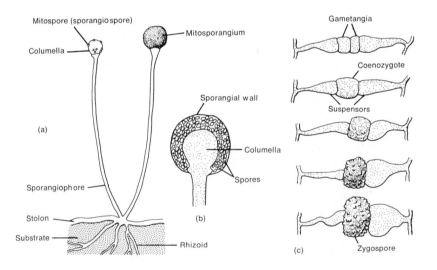

**Figure 3-9.** *Rhizopus.* (a) Hyphal differentiation and asexual reproduction. (b) Details of the nearly mature sporangium. (c) Stages in formation of coenozygote.

lateral branches develop and come together. The directed growth of the hyphal tips indicates the involvement of hormones during the sexual reproductive process. Upon contact, the tip of each hypha is cut off by a crosswall to form a multinucleate gametangium. The cell walls between adjacent plus and minus gametangia dissolve and the protoplasts of the two cells fuse to form a coenozygote. The coenozygote develops a thick, black, warty wall—at which time it is called a zygospore (Fig. 3-9c). The length of the dormant period depends on the environmental conditions, but generally it lasts at least one month. Meiosis occurs upon zygospore germination, and a single sporangiophore emerges from the ruptured zygospore. The nonflagellated haploid spores are wind-disseminated and, upon germination, give rise to the haploid vegetative mycelium of the plant.

### Pilobolus

Mention has been made that fungi live on practically all known organic substrates, and the dung of animals is no exception. One of the most remarkable of these coprophilous (copros = dung; philos = loving) fungi is *Pilobolus*, an organism common on the dung of herbivores such as cows and horses. Although many coprophilous fungi show some modifications for their habitat, *Pilobolus* exhibits an amazing specialization in the form and function of its sporangial apparatus (sporangium plus sporangiophore). Not only does the sporangiophore bend toward light (positive phototropism) but, at maturity, the whole sporangium is forcibly shot away by a "water-squirt" mechanism. The mature sporangial apparatus prior to discharge is shown in Fig. 3-10.

The sporangiophore is a remarkable example of cell specialization for function. It is the structure responsible for the directed and forcible discharge of the sporangium. The sporangiophore arises from a bulbous base (the *trophocyst*) at or near the level of the substrate. Unlike *Rhizopus*, *Pilobolus* has a crosswall separating the sporangiophore from the rest of the hypha. The upper end of the sporangiophore is enlarged, forming a subsporangial swelling. An orange carotenoid pigment occurs at the base of the subsporangial swelling and is involved in the positive phototropic behavior of the sporangiophore. Protoplasm within the subsporangial swelling is restricted to a thin peripheral layer by a large central aqueous vacuole.

When the sporangial apparatus is mature there is an increase of osmotically active sugars in the sporangiophore, and this results in an increase in the water pressure in the cell. A line of weakness, where the carbohydrate cell wall is thinner, occurs around the upper part of the subsporangial swelling just below the sporangium (Fig. 3-10a). When the water pressure exceeds the restraining strength of the carbohydrate wall, the sporangiophore bursts (with an audible "pop") at the line of weakness, shooting away the sporangium for distances up to eight feet. (*Pilobolus* literally means "hat-thrower.") The photo-orientation of the sporangiophore makes it almost certain that the sporangium will be shot clear of the substrate.

The sporangium also shows specialization. The upper part of the sporangium wall is black in color and is heavily impregnated with waxy compounds. Within the sporangium, spores are in the upper part and a ring of mucilage is below (Fig. 3-10b). The sporangium wall near the base of the sporangium

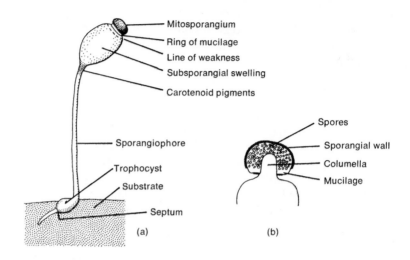

**Figure 3-10.** *Pilobolus.* (a) Mature sporangial apparatus. (b) Section through anterior end of (a) to show relationship of mitosporangium and mucilage to the columella.

breaks immediately prior to discharge, exposing the mucilage. The mucilage is shot away with the sporangium and serves to affix the discharged sporangium upon contact with an object. The fact that the upper surface of the sporangium is nonwettable insures that the upper surface will bob to the surface of the sticky drop and remain in this orientation upon drying. In this position the black coloration of the upper part of the sporangium will help prevent light damage to the colorless spores, and the waxy surface will help prevent desiccation of the thin-walled spores.

When the object to which the sporangium becomes affixed is a leaf or stem of an herbaceous plant, there is a good chance that the sporangium will be eaten by a herbivore. The spores are not injured as they pass through the digestive tract of the animal; in fact, the physiology of the spores is altered so that they are capable of germination. Spore germination in the excreted dung again initiates the developmental cycle of *Pilobolus*.

Collection of *Pilobolus* and other coprophilous fungi is simple providing one has access to a pastured horse or cow. Fresh dung (the fresher the better, since *Pilobolus* is one of the first fungi to appear) is placed in a glass dish lined with moist paper toweling, and the dish is covered with a loosely fitting lid. The dish should be kept in a cool room out of direct sunlight, but where it receives a day-night cycle. In fresh dung, *Pilobolus* appears in about seven days. At intervals a succession of other fungi (Zygomycetes, Ascomycetes, and Basidiomycetes) follows.

### Ascomycetes

The Ascomycetes (askos = bladder or sac) form a very large group that contains many economically important fungi. Most of the blue-green, red, and brown molds that cause food spoilage are Ascomycetes. Many, including the powdery mildews, are plant parasites. Ergot of rye, one of the oldest known plant diseases and one recognized by the Greeks and Romans, is caused by the fungus *Claviceps purpurea*. Infection of the rye plant by the fungus occurs at the time of flowering and results in the replacement of kernels of rye by a hard, black fungal growth that contains several potent alkaloids. Although they may cause gangrene and death if eaten in large amounts, these alkaloids have important medicinal uses. They are used in the control of hemorrhage, especially during childbirth, and in treating migraine.

Another Ascomycete, of more recent notoriety, causes the Dutch elm disease. Accidental introduction of the fungus *Ceratocystis ulmi* into the United States is gradually eradicating the American elm, one of our most beautiful shade trees. This particular fungus has been difficult to control because it lives within the tree, where sprays cannot reach it. Its spread is due to bark-boring beetles, which carry fungal spores from tree to tree. Most control measures have been directed toward the beetle but, except in a few cases, have been largely unsuccessful.

Although few Ascomycetes are used as food, the morels and truffles are more highly prized by gourmets than are mushrooms (which are Basidiomycetes). Unfortunately it has so far been impossible to induce in culture the edible reproductive structures of morels and truffles for commerce. Truffles are of particular interest because they are found below the soil surface in presumed mycorrhizal association with trees such as oaks. Because they grow below the soil surface, they are often difficult to find, for although these fungi have a characteristic odor, man's sense of smell is too poorly developed to detect it. Therefore in France and Italy pigs and dogs have been trained for truffle hunting. Our native truffles, found by hand sifting of soil, are usually quite small, but large imported ones may be purchased in gourmet sections of many stores in the United States.

---

Except in a few cases (such as the yeasts) in which the plant body is unicellular, Ascomycetes are typically mycelial with chitinous walls. New cells arise by the forward growth of hyphal tips, with subsequent ingrowth of septa behind the tips. The septa do not form complete partitions, however; a central pore remains which allows for cytoplasmic interchange between adjacent cells as well as for movement of both mitochondria and nuclei (Fig. 3-11). The pore may be closed by a plug of material during later growth. The cells are uninucleate in some Ascomycetes; in others they are multinucleate. The mitotic spindle is intranuclear, as it is in many other fungi.

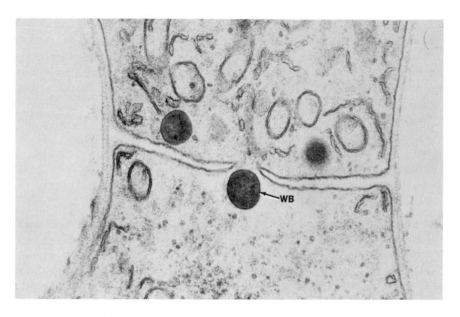

**Figure 3-11.**  Section of vegetative hypha of the Ascomycete *Saccobolus uerverni*, showing perforate septum and Woronin body (WB). Note continuity of the cell membrane between adjacent cells. Courtesy of Dr. G. C. Carroll, University of Oregon, Eugene.

While there is general uniformity in hyphal structure in this group, there is great morphological diversity among reproductive bodies. Several types of asexual reproductive structures are known, each of which is adapted to a particular function. The *conidium*, a type of mitospore, is the most common type. Conidia are uninucleate, nonflagellated cells cut off in chains from tips of modified hyphae called *conidiophores*. Airborne conidia are characteristic of many common food-spoilage fungi such as *Aspergillus* and *Penicillium* (Fig. 3-12).

The form of the sexual reproductive structures, called ascocarps (carp = fruit), is variable. But before these structures are discussed, the sexual process

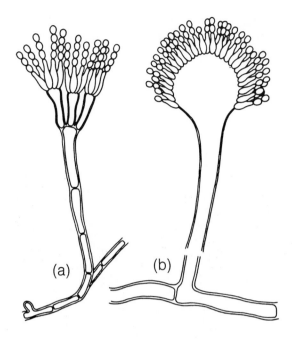

**Figure 3-12.** (a) Conidiophore of *Penicillium*. (b) Section of a conidiophore of *Aspergillus*. From Scagel et al., *Plant Diversity: An Evolutionary Approach*, Wadsworth Publishing Co., 1969. Reproduced by permission of the publisher and the authors.

in Ascomycetes will first be described (Fig. 3-13). The female sex organ is called the *ascogonium* (gonium is the root of gignesthai, meaning to be born). This cell is partially or completely embedded in a hyphal mat. A short filament, called the *trichogyne,* to which the male sex organ becomes attached, may also be present on the ascogonium. If a trichogyne is absent, the male sex organ attaches directly to the ascogonium. The antheridium is the male sex organ of many Ascomycetes. After attachment of the antheridium to the ascogonium or trichogyne, the cell wall disappears at the point of contact and the one or more nuclei of the male cell move into the ascogonium. Nuclear pairing occurs but fusion does not occur. Instead, the paired nuclei divide mitotically, and hyphal filaments grow out from the ascogonium. Each cell of these filaments contains one nucleus of each parental type. The condition in which a cell contains two paired nuclei, one from each parent, is called *dikaryotic.* Although nuclear fusion has not occurred, dikaryotic cells are functionally diploid and show the type of dominance and recessiveness that one would expect from truly diploid cells. Cells that contain one or more nuclei, but all of the same type, are called *monokaryotic.*

Fusion of the male and female sex organs stimulates the monokaryotic hyphae of the mycelial mat surrounding the ascogonium to grow out and give rise to the ascocarp. As indicated in Fig. 3-13, most of the ascocarp is made up

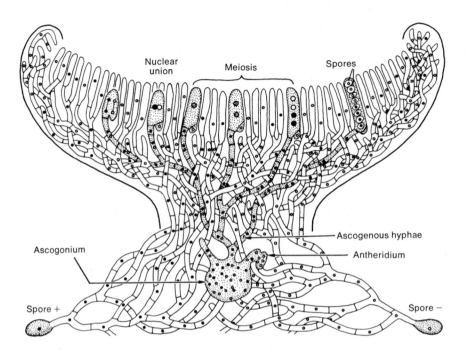

**Figure 3-13.** Diagram of the structure of an ascocarp. Ascogonium = female cell; antheridium = male cell; ascogenous hyphae = dikaryotic hyphae. From L. W. Sharp, *Fundamentals of Cytology*, McGraw-Hill Book Co., Inc., 1943. Reproduced by permission of the publisher.

of monokaryotic hyphae. The dikaryotic hyphae grow up and through the monokaryotic hyphae. At maturity, the penultimate cells of dikaryotic hyphae form sac-like structures called *asci* (singular: *ascus*), usually in specific regions of the ascocarp. The form of the ascocarp is a diagnostic feature of many fungi in this group. However, the directed and integrated growth of dikaryotic and monokaryotic hyphae has not yet been fully investigated.

Three general types of ascocarps are recognized: *apothecium, perithecium,* and *cleistothecium* (Fig. 3-14). The apothecium basically is cup-shaped (as in *Peziza*), and asci line the inner surface of the cup. The convoluted ascocarps of morels and truffles are considered to be modifications of the apothecium. The perithecium is usually a flask-shaped structure with a neck and an apical

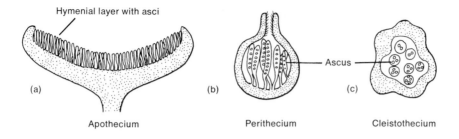

Hymenial layer with asci

Ascus

(a)            (b)            (c)

Apothecium        Perithecium        Cleistothecium

**Figure 3-14.** Three common types of Ascomycete ascocarps.

opening. In this type, asci develop at the base and the ascospores are discharged through the apical pore. The fungi that cause ergot of rye and Dutch elm disease have perithecial ascocarps. The third type of ascocarp, the cleistothecium, is completely enclosed, and asci are scattered throughout the interior. A common example of a fungus with cleistothecia is *Microsphaeria,* which causes powdery mildew of lilac.

The ascus is the definitive characteristic of Ascomycetes. In most Ascomycetes it is the subterminal cell of a dikaryotic hypha in which nuclear fusion, meiosis, and spore development occur (Fig. 3-15). During ascus development, the terminal cell of a dikaryotic hypha bends back at the tip and the nuclei divide. Cell wall formation occurs in such a way as to form a monokaryotic terminal cell and third cell from the apex, and a dikaryotic subterminal cell. The nuclei in the subterminal cell then fuse and this is immediately followed by meiosis; the true diploid stage is very short. In most cases, each of the four haploid nuclei then undergoes one mitotic division, forming eight nuclei in each ascus. Cleavage of cytoplasm around each nucleus is followed by deposition of a rigid wall, forming a total of eight meiospores per ascus (Fig. 3-15). In mycological terminology these spores are called *ascospores,* in recognition of the manner and place of their formation.

Ascospores, to be effective in dissemination of the fungus to new areas, must be discharged from the ascocarp. Discharge may be passive, or, as in the case of most Ascomycetes, active. Active discharge results in the forcible ejection of the ascospores from the ascus. Cytoplasm excluded from spores during ascospore formation is usually involved in active spore discharge. The interested student is encouraged to read a small, delightfully written book by C. T. Ingold, on spore dispersal mechanisms in fungi (see Suggestions for Further Reading).

Of the several Ascomycetes that are important research organisms, the pink bread mold *Neurospora* is worthy of special mention because of its prominence in genetic and biochemical investigations. The developmental cycle of this

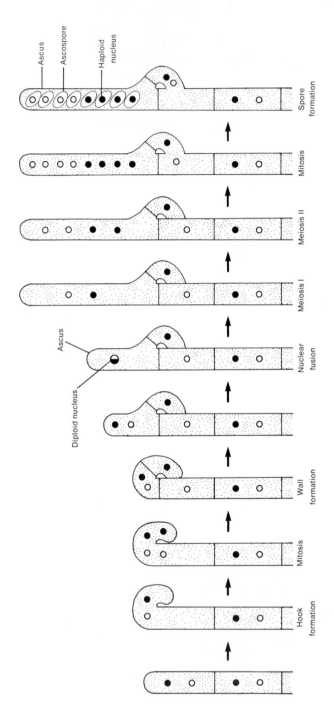

**Figure 3-15.** Ascus and ascospore development.

fungus is essentially similar to that given above; it is mycelial, forms conidia, and produces asci within perithecia as a result of sexual reproduction. Its main vegetative phase is haploid; thus any gene mutation is immediately expressed, and its short generation time speeds genetic investigations. *Neurospora* grows readily on a chemically defined medium; therefore biochemical mutants, easily induced by X-radiation, are simply characterized. Plants used in genetic investigations are hermaphroditic but heterothallic (that is, sexual structures produced on the same thallus are self-incompatible). The eight ascospores are produced in a single row within a relatively narrow ascus; by means of micro-manipulation it is possible to isolate and culture separately the progeny of each ascospore. Thus, not only is it possible to study all products of a single meiotic division (which is not possible in animals or flowering plants), but the linear spatial arrangement of the ascospores enables us to study the results of the first and second meiotic divisions.

While *Neurospora* and *Peziza* may be considered "typical" Ascomycetes, there are some, such as brewer's yeast (*Saccharomyces cerevisiae*), that are unicellular and lack a fruiting body. In brewer's yeast, the individual cells themselves are transformed into asci and produce ascospores under appropriate conditions. In addition, this and many other yeasts form new cells in a manner unlike that of most other plants, by a process termed *budding*. New cells arise by the origin and development of a small bud on one side of the parent cell. Nuclear division occurs and one nucleus moves into the enlarging bud. The bud is ultimately cut off from the mother cell and the two cells separate (Fig. 3-16).

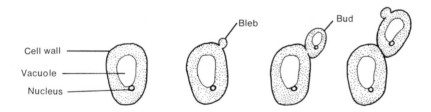

**Figure 3-16.**   Budding of yeast cells.

Many studies have been directed toward understanding the mechanics of budding in yeasts. Time-lapse motion picture studies have shown that buds are initiated by a sudden extrusion of naked protoplasm through a hole in the yeast cell wall. In contrast to enzymatically induced naked protoplasts (discussed earlier with bacterial cell walls), which cannot synthesize new cell walls, bud protoplasts are quickly covered by wall material. It is pertinent to note that wall synthesis begins adjacent to the wall of the mother cell, indicating the need for a "primer" of pre-existing wall substance for wall synthesis. It has been found that a specific area of the yeast cell is involved in bud initiation (see Nickerson in Suggestions for Further Reading). There appears to be a localized softening of the wall in this area followed by a protoplasmic blowout. Use of radioactive compounds has shown that bud-forming areas are high in sulfhydral groups (-SH), and wall softening is interpreted as resulting from enzymatic reduction of disulfide bonds (—S—S—) to form sulfhydral groups. Results from numerous studies on yeast budding and on mold-yeast dimorphism (described previously) have led to the suggestion that hyphal branching and yeast budding are different morphological manifestations of similar underlying physiological processes.

### Basidiomycetes

Basidiomycetes (basidium, diminutive of basis = base) are the fungi most commonly seen in fields and forests and along wooded streams. They include the mushrooms, toadstools, puffballs, and bracket or shelf fungi (Fig. 3-17). Many of these are saprobic or mycorrhizal fungi. This group also includes the rusts and smuts, which are obligate parasites on many vital economic plants.

Basidiomycetes have many points of similarity with the Ascomycetes, including central pores in the hyphal septa (Fig. 3-18). However, whereas the Ascomycetes have monokaryotic vegetative hyphae, Basidiomycetes have vegetative mycelia usually composed of dikaryotic, functionally diploid hyphae. Hyphal differentiation into asexual reproductive structures, including conidia, is generally similar to that in Ascomycetes, although many Basidiomycetes appear to have lost the capacity for asexual reproduction.

The *basidium,* generally a club-shaped structure, is the definitive characteristic of Basidiomycetes. Like the ascus, the basidium is a cell in which nuclear fusion and meiosis occurs. However, the spores of the basidium are formed externally, outside of the basidium proper. After meiosis, the haploid nuclei migrate out into each of four small blebs on the distal end of the basidium. Upon enlargement, these blebs mature into sterigmata and meiospores called *basidiospores* (Fig. 3-19). Two types of basidia are found in the Basidiomycetes: (1) unicellular and (2) septate. Basidia of mushrooms, puffballs, and bracket fungi are unicellular; those of rusts and smuts are septate. The development of a mushroom and a rust are discussed below.

### Mushrooms

The term *mushroom* usually refers only to edible Basidiomycetes that have a fruiting body differentiated into cap, stipe, and gills. *Toadstool* usually refers to morphologically similar but inedible varieties. There is no dividing line, however, between mushrooms and toadstools. While some fungi are deadly

**Figure 3-17.** Basidiocarps of basidiomycetes. (a)–(c) Mushrooms. (a) *Agaricus*. Note the large annulus (A). (b) *Coprinus,* or "shaggy mane" mushroom; the mature cap undergoes autodigestion, forming an inky-black substance. (c) *Amanita;* most species of this genus are poisonous. Note the numerous scales on the cap of the basidiocarp. (d) *Clavaria*. The basidia line the outer surface of these erect basidiocarps. (e) Puffball. The basidiospores develop enclosed within the basidiocarp. (f) Bracket fungi (*Polystictus*). The basidia line pores on the lower surface of these basidiocarps. Photos (b)–(f) courtesy of Mr. Al Lowry, Santa Cruz, California.

**Fungi**                                                                                                          **61**

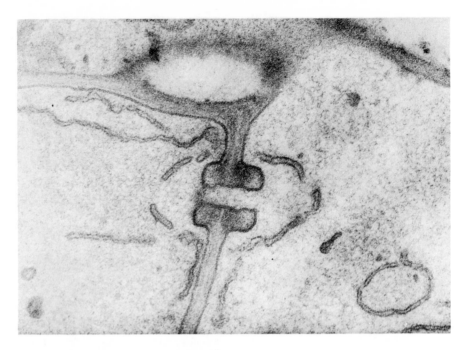

**Figure 3-18.** Septal pore at the base of the basidium of *Schizophyllum commune*. Note the continuity of the cell membrane between adjacent cells and the arrangement of the endoplasmic reticulum in the vicinity of the septal pore. Courtesy of Dr. K. Wells, University of California, Davis.

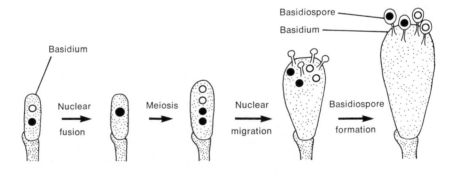

**Figure 3-19.** Basidium and basidiospore development.

poisonous, there are others that are poisonous to one person but may be eaten by another with no ill effects. Moreover, many edible mushrooms are closely related to poisonous ones: poisonous and nonpoisonous species may occur in the same genus. Therefore mushrooms as discussed in this book include both poisonous and nonpoisonous forms.

As previously mentioned, the main vegetative phase of growth of Basidiomycetes is by dikaryotic hyphae. In contrast to many Ascomycetes, there are no morphologically differentiated sex organs. Dikaryotic hyphae are often established by hyphal fusions between different strains (plus and minus) in heterothallic forms. (There are several other ways, not discussed here, in which a dikaryon may be established in mushrooms.) Once formed, the dikaryon usually is long-lived, living from one to many years, but because it grows within the substrate it is seldom seen. Periodically (in the spring for some fungi, and in the late summer or fall for others), fruiting bodies are initiated. As yet, little is known about the physiological changes occurring within the hyphae during the initiation of the reproductive phase.

Basidiocarp initiation occurs when a localized region of the mycelium begins active growth to give rise to a tightly appressed mass of hyphae referred to as a "button." Enlargement of the button, primarily by water uptake, leads to the formation of the mature basidiocarp (Fig. 3-20a–c). Basidia line both surfaces of the gills and the basidiospores are forcibly shot away from the gills when mature. Subsequently, spores are normally dispersed by wind currents.

A single mycelium generally gives rise to more than one basidiocarp in mushrooms. Thus the greater the extent of mycelial growth of the vegetative mycelium within the substrate, with its greater food-absorbing potential, the larger the number of mushrooms initiated. In comparison with Ascomycetes, in which a single sexual act normally results in the formation of a single ascocarp, we find that a single sexual act in mushrooms (and other Basidiomycetes) yields many basidiocarps.

The origin and development of mushrooms and of other types of basidiocarps include morphogenetic processes that we are just beginning to understand. The basidiocarp is composed of a multitude of individual hyphae. What controls and integrates their growth rate so that the characteristic form and structure of the fruiting body invariably results? Although not completely

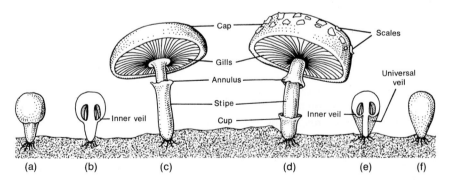

**Figure 3-20.** Mushroom-type of basidiocarps. (a–c) *Agaricus* type: (a) button stage; (b) section through button; (c) mature basidiocarp. (d–f) *Amanita* type: (f) button stage; (e) section through button; (d) mature fruiting body.

understood, it has long been recognized that light often has a formative effect. In total darkness there is no development of the cap. Moreover, it has been found that the presence of gills greatly promotes expansion of the cap in one mushroom. The possible involvement of hormones in regulation of growth and development of basidiocarps awaits further study.

Some mushrooms, such as the poisonous *Amanita*, possess an additional structure. The immature basidiocarp of these mushrooms is enclosed by a thin membrane called a *universal veil*. Remnants of this veil often remain as scales on the cap and as a basal cup on the mature mushroom (Fig. 3-20d–f). However, presence of scales or of a cup does not automatically designate a poisonous mushroom, since some that have the universal veil are edible, while many poisonous mushrooms lack it.

The basidiocarps of puffballs, which are edible before spore formation, originate like mushrooms. They differ structurally in that the basidia and basidiospores remain enclosed at maturity. Various methods have evolved to ensure spore dispersal. In some puffballs — such as the giant puffball *Calvatia*, which may measure over 45 centimeters in diameter — the outer layer disintegrates and the spores are passively dispersed by the wind. Other puffballs have a basidiocarp with an apical pore, which functions like a small bellows, when hit by a drop of rain; it puffs out clouds of spores that are then wind-dispersed. Perhaps the most elaborate spore-discharge mechanism in this group belongs to *Sphaerobolus* (literally, "sphere thrower"). In this fungus, discharge is effected by the catapulting of the entire spore mass (about 2 mm in diameter) to a distance of about 5 meters (for details, see Ingold in Suggestions for Further Reading).

### Rusts

Rusts differ from mushrooms, puffballs, and bracket fungi in that they have septate basidia, their basidia are not developed in a basidiocarp, and they have morphologically differentiated male and female sex cells. Rusts are obligate plant parasites and are of particular importance to man because they attack many of man's economic plants, including the cereal grains. The life cycle of rusts is complex. Some require a single host to complete their life history; that is, they are *autoecious* (autos = self; oikia = dwelling). Other rusts, on the other hand, are *heteroecious* (heteros = other); two different hosts are required for the fungus to complete its normal development. Since many rusts form five different types of spores during their development, it is not surprising to find that there is an elaborate terminology associated with these fungi. A knowledge of this terminology is prerequisite to the understanding of the development and biology of rusts.

Probably for Western man the most important rust is *Puccinia graminis*, a heteroecious rust that causes the black stem rust of wheat and other grains.

Wheat is the basis of Western civilization. Our greatest competitor for wheat, as well as for several other cereal grains, is *Puccinia graminis* and its various strains. The wheat rust is found everywhere that wheat is grown, and is a continual source of economic loss for the wheat grower. The fungus destroys chlorophyll and uses the sugars synthesized by the wheat, resulting in a smaller than normal grain size and reduced grain yield per acre. Because of its direct influence on our economy, the life history of the wheat rust is discussed here in detail.

Perhaps the best place to begin such a discussion is with the haploid basidiospore. The basidiospore is formed during the spring of the year and it infects the other host of this heteroecious rust, the common barberry plant. (This is not to be confused with the Japanese barberry, a commonly cultivated and nonsusceptible ornamental shrub.) Basidiospore germination results in the development of monokaryotic hyphae that invade the tissue of the barberry plant. Soon a small, flask-shaped pustule, called a *spermagonium* (spermo = seed, germ; gone = offspring), is formed on the upper surface of the barberry leaf (Fig. 3-21a). In addition to forming spermagonia, monokaryotic hyphae grow toward the lower leaf surface and form structures called *aecia primordia* (aikia = injury). Aecia primordia, which are initially monokaryotic, do not develop further until they become dikaryotic.

Establishment of the dikaryon is the function of the spermagonium. Within the cavity of the spermagonium, small cells called spermatia bud off, much like conidia, from short hyphal branches. In addition, long hyphae, called *receptive hyphae*, form around the opening of the spermagonium (Fig. 3-21a). Spermatia and receptive hyphae formed by a single mycelium are self-incompatible. Moreover, the spermagonia fall into two mating types, + and −. Dikaryotization occurs only when a + spermatium is transferred to a − receptive hypha, or vice versa. At maturity, spermatia extrude from the spermagonium in a drop of sugar-water solution. Flies and other insects are attracted to the sugary drop of liquid, and their movements result in the transfer of a spermatium from one spermagonium to a receptive hypha of another. The cell wall is dissolved at the point of contact and the spermatial nucleus migrates into the receptive hypha, and, presumably, through the hypha to the aecia primordium. The details of nuclear movement are not clear because it has been impossible to follow this *in vivo*. It is known that the cells of the aecium become dikaryotic after spermatial fusion with the receptive hypha. Soon thereafter, dikaryotic *aeciospores* are budded off in chains and are dispersed by the wind (Fig. 3-21a). Although formed on the barberry, aeciospores are unable to reinfect the barberry; they can infect only the wheat plant.

Formation of spermagonia and aecia is quite rapid and, by late spring, airborne aeciospores begin to infect the wheat. Aeciospores germinate and dikaryotic hyphae penetrate through the stomata and grow within the wheat plant. Soon, localized areas of hyphal growth rupture the host's epidermis, and another type of spore, the *uredospore,* is formed at the tips of short hyphal branches (Fig. 3-21b). The brownish-red coloration of the uredospores, which are dikaryotic, gives the characteristic rust color to this stage of infection. Uredospores are continuously produced during the summer. They cause a rapid population buildup in the field in a short period of time and they carry the fungus to new fields. The spores are light and are well adapted for airborne dispersal.

Toward fall, as the wheat plant matures, hyphal metabolism is altered and a new kind of spore, the *teliospore* (telios = end, completion), is formed. These spores are formed either in the same lesions that earlier produced uredospores, or in new lesions. Teliospores are black, and they are responsible for the common name, "black stem rust of wheat," of this fungus. They are two-celled spores and are thick-walled, resistant structures that help the fungus survive during the winter (Fig. 3-21c). Teliospores are particularly important in northern wheat-growing regions, where the winters may be quite invigorating. Nuclear fusion occurs soon after teliospore formation, and the fungus overwinters in

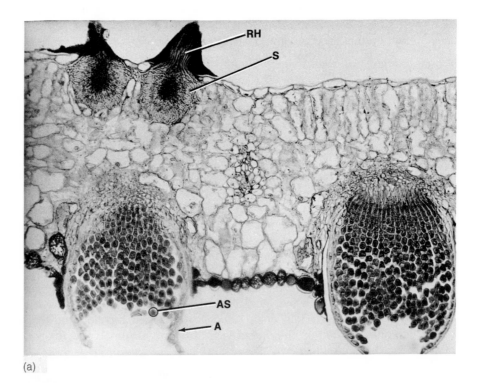

(a)

**Figure 3-21.** *Puccinia graminis.* (a) Spermagonia and aecia on barberry leaf; spermagonium (S); receptive hyphae (RH); aecium (A); aeciospore (AS). (b) Uredospore formation on wheat; note destruction of host tissue; u.: uredospore. (c) Teliospore formation on wheat; teliospore (two-celled) (T).

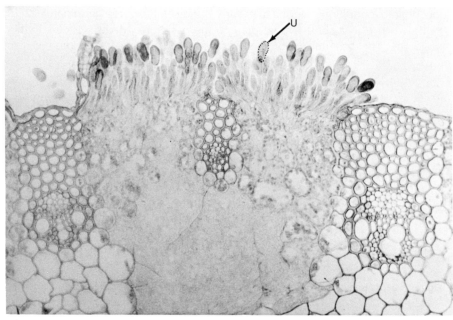

(b)

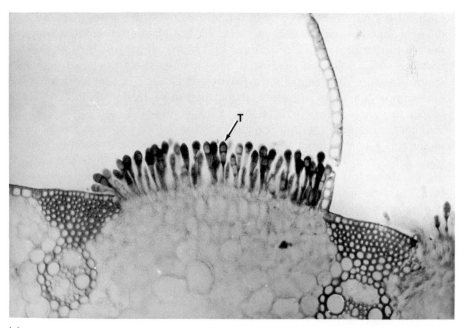

(c)

the diploid condition. During the early spring, teliospores germinate; each cell gives rise to a short hyphal branch, the basidium. Meiosis occurs in the basidium. The basidium soon becomes septate, and each cell produces a

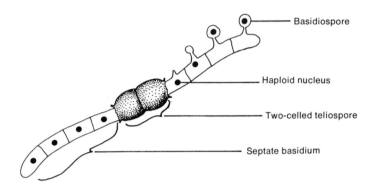

Basidiospore

Haploid nucleus

Two-celled teliospore

Septate basidium

**Figure 3-22.** Basidium and basidiospore development of the rust *Gymnosporangium.*

single, haploid basidiospore (Fig. 3-22). Subsequent basidiospore discharge and barberry infection repeats the life cycle of the wheat rust.

*Puccinia graminis* is a remarkable organism. Not only does it require two hosts for normal development, but it produces five spore types, each with a different function, within one year (Fig. 3-23). Clearly, the understanding of the life history of parasitic organisms such as the wheat rust is of prime importance to pathologists, because it often enables them to suggest efficient control measures. The adaptation to two different hosts is not unique in biology. For example, the malarial parasite spends part of its life in man and part of its life in the female mosquito. In the case of the wheat rust, the suggested solution was to eradicate the common barberry, since it is economically unimportant. A considerable amount of money and energy has been expended toward this goal, and there has been significant success in reducing the amount of annual crop loss. On the other hand, complete control has not been achieved. Why not? The answer comes from understanding the biology of the rust over its entire range in North America. Barberry eradication, which broke the normal developmental cycle of the fungus, did not completely control rust infestation, because in the southern limits of the wheat belt (the southern United States and Mexico) winters are mild enough to permit the survival of the rust in the uredospore stage. Consequently, these areas serve as reservoirs for infection; uredospores are blown progressively northward during spring and summer as temperatures become favorable for wheat germination and growth in the northern areas. Thus although barberry eradication has cut down the magnitude of annual loss considerably, it has not completely controlled the wheat rust.

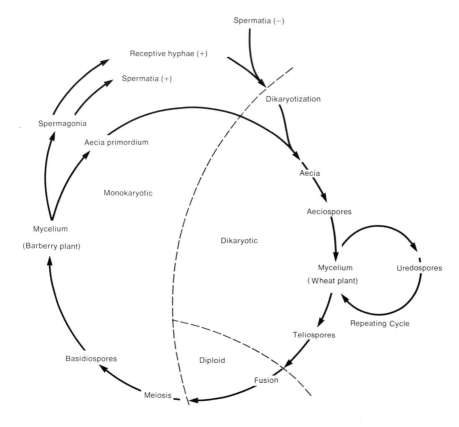

Spermatia (−)

Receptive hyphae (+)

Spermatia (+)

Dikaryotization

Spermagonia

Aecia primordium

Aecia

Monokaryotic

Aeciospores

Mycelium

(Barberry plant)

Dikaryotic

Mycelium          Uredospores

(Wheat plant)

Repeating Cycle

Teliospores

Basidiospores          Diploid

Fusion

Meiosis

**Figure 3-23.**    Life cycle of the wheat rust, *Puccinia graminis.*

Recent attempts to control wheat rust have been undertaken through genetics, by the breeding of more rust-resistant varieties of wheat. The rust, however, is still not completely controlled, since an entirely rust-resistant variety of commercial wheat has not been developed. A variety of wheat is considered to be rust-resistant if it is resistant to the race of wheat rust *predominant* in an area at that particular time. Wheat rust is not a genetically homogeneous population, but consists of many physiologically different races, and new races constantly arise through recombination during sexual reproduction and by random mutations. Therefore it is only a matter of time before a population buildup of a race compatible with the new variety of wheat occurs, creating an epidemic. At this time, a new "rust-resistant" variety of wheat must be available to the farmer. This is the present situation, a never ending fight to stay at least one resistant strain of wheat ahead of the rust. (Turning to rice as a food base is no solution, since it too is parasitized by competitive rust fungi.) The significance of this battle will be heightened as the world's food problem continues to increase. Continued population increase, in this country and in others, will place heavy demands on agricultural expertise. This is an excellent argument in support of the continued relevance to our society of agriculture experiment stations and agriculture-oriented colleges.

It is also of interest to note in passing that the use of resistant varieties of wheat (and other cereal grains) curtails the survival of most races of the wheat rust. Only compatible races are selected from the genetically heterogeneous fungal population. This type of directed selection of physiological races has been called man-guided evolution.

The wheat rust is but one of a very large assemblage of rust fungi. Rusts on plants of roses, hollyhocks, carnations, and snapdragons are well known to home gardeners. One rust (called *Gymnosporangium juniperi-virginianae*) attacks junipers and uses the apple and the crab apple as alternate hosts. Structures called "cedar-apples," which represent a mixture of mycelium and host tissue, develop on the juniper. In the spring, teliospores are extruded from the cedar-apples in elongate, orange, mucilagenous masses. Spermagonia and aecia develop on the apple and crab apple. Uredospores, the repeating stage, are not formed by this fungus, and the developmental cycle is broken when junipers and apples or crab apples are not planted in close proximity.

The white pine blister rust (*Cronartium ribicola*) is a fungus of relatively recent notoriety in North America. It was accidently introduced into North America from Europe and has threatened to eradicate the native stands of eastern and western white pine. The spermagonial and aecial stages occur on the white pine, while the uredospore and teliospore stages occur on the economically unimportant alternate hosts, the currants and gooseberries. Since there is no way for the aeciospores to reinfect the white pine, the rust is controlled simply by getting rid of the currants and gooseberries, both of which are species of the genus *Ribes*. The continuing campaign to eradicate these plants and thereby to control the spread of the fungus is quite successful.

## Summary

| Group | Flagella | Place of Meiosis |
|---|---|---|
| Chytridiomycetes | One posterior whiplash | Resistant meiosporangium or zygospore |
| Oomycetes | One whiplash and one tinsel | Antheridium and oogonium (?) |
| Zygomycetes | None | Zygospore |
| Ascomycetes | None | Ascus |
| Basidiomycetes | None | Basidium |

*Additional:* eukaryotic cellular structure; nonphotosynthetic and heterotrophic.

## Evolutionary Relationships

There are at least four theories on the origin of fungi: (1) fungi evolved from filamentous bacteria; (2) fungi evolved from algae with the loss of photosynthetic pigments; (3) fungi evolved from protozoa; and (4) fungi evolved independently of bacteria, algae, and protozoa and are neither plants nor animals — they represent a third kingdom of organisms. While it is not possible here to discuss these theories in great detail, the following comments are pertinent to an understanding of fungal relationships.

There has been growing recognition that the class Phycomycetes represented an artificial grouping of unrelated organisms. Plants placed here have the same general level of thallus organization. That is, the relatively simple thallus is generally nonseptate and flagellated cells are produced by many. Moreover, mitospores are usually produced in sporangia and the sexual reproductive processes are generally straightforward. With the emphasis in recent years on flagellation (in combination with other features) as an important phylogenetic criterion, the Phycomycetes have been separated into six more or less distinct classes. Three of these classes (Chytridiomycetes, Oomycetes, and Zygomycetes) are discussed in this book.

The presence of a single, posterior, whiplash flagellum in members of the class Chytridiomycetes isolates these fungi from other fungi, and from most other organisms. This type of flagellar insertion is not characteristic of any algal or protozoan group. Moreover, the Chytridiomycetes are dissimilar to other fungi in many additional respects, and the suggestion that they should be placed in a separate division has some merit.

The Oomycetes have two flagella, one of the whiplash and one of the tinsel type. In this characteristic, Oomycetes are similar to brown, yellow-green, and golden algae. Considering all characteristics, the yellow-green and golden algae appear to be more promising progenitors than brown algae (see Chapter 8). Specifically, the multinucleate, nonseptate filamentous thallus of *Vaucheria*, a yellow-green alga, greatly resembles the thallus of some Oomycetes. Moreover, the reproductive structures of *Vaucheria* and some Oomycetes are somewhat similar. However, there are other characteristics, including the chemical nature of the cell wall, that argue against a close relationship, if any at all, between Oomycetes and *Vaucheria*. Thus the ancestry of the Oomycetes remains uncertain.

The Zygomycetes are predominantly terrestrial fungi, and they lack flagellated cells in their life histories. Some students of mycology have suggested that Zygomycetes evolved from Oomycetes. In this view, the Zygomycetes are seen as the culmination of an aquatic to terrestrial series that occurs in the Oomycetes. Although *Saprolegnia* (described earlier) is aquatic, several other genera illustrate partial to complete adaptation to terrestrial life, as measured by the loss of flagellated mitospores. For example, mitospores of *Phytophthora infestans* and *Plasmopara viticola* are flagellated when water is available, and nonflagellated when free water is not present. This is considered to be a transitional stage leading to the complete absence of dependence on water for spore dispersal and germination. Spores of the related genus *Peronospora* are always nonflagellated; they have completely lost the ability to form flagellated cells. Nonetheless, many mycologists consider it doubtful that Zygomycetes represent the culmination of the aquatic (flagellated) to terrestrial (nonflagellated) series found in the Oomycetes.

At least three theories have been advanced to explain the origin of Ascomycetes. First, some have suggested that they evolved from filamentous bacteria (the Actinomycetes) that form conidia-like spores. However, the great difference in cellular structure (prokaryotic versus eukaryotic) argues against this relationship.

A second theory is that Ascomycetes evolved from Zygomycetes. In one small group of Zygomycetes (the Endogonaceae, not discussed in this book), the sexual reproductive structures become surrounded by sterile hyphae, forming a reproductive body. Since this could be considered the forerunner of the ascocarp, some mycologists have suggested the origin of Ascomycetes from similar zygomycetous fungi. Conversely, the Zygomycetes could have evolved from the Ascomycetes.

The third theory is that Ascomycetes evolved from red algae with the loss of photosynthetic pigments. (See Denison and Carroll, Selected Readings, for an extended discussion.) The Ascomycetes have several characteristics in common with red algae (especially parasitic red algae). Both groups lack flagellated cells, and there is no evidence that they evolved from flagellated ancestors. The mitotic spindle is intranuclear and the filamentous type of thallus construction is common in both groups. Moreover, cells of the thallus are connected by pores that may be plugged with material in later development. Finally, the form of the reproductive structures is similar. There is a major difference, however, in cell wall chemistry (chitin in Ascomycetes and cellulose in red algae). Nonetheless, this is an attractive theory and deserves continued comparative research. Particularly, more information is needed on parasitic red algae and marine ascomycetes.

Basidiomycetes and Ascomycetes show considerable similarity during the development of the basidium and basidiospores and the ascus and ascospores. Conidia are also present in both groups, and their cell wall chemistry is quite similar. These similarities have led many mycologists to suggest that the Basidiomycetes evolved from the Ascomycetes, or that they evolved from a common ancestor.

In summary, it is evident that there is still no general agreement on the relationships of fungi to other organisms or to each other. The view favored by this author is that the division Eumycota is an unnatural group as presently constituted. The Zygomycetes, Ascomycetes, and Basidiomycetes appear to be related by descent. On the other hand, the relationships of the Oomycetes and Chytridiomycetes still need clarification and these organisms are here maintained in the division Eumycota only for convenience and until additional information becomes available. Information is needed at all levels (from descriptive morphology to biochemical processes) of investigation, since detailed studies have been carried out on so few organisms.

# 4

## Slime Molds

Slime molds, or Myxomycota (myxa = slime; mykes = fungus) form a small group having practically no economic importance. Nonetheless, slime molds are of considerable interest to biologists. They are very useful experimental organisms, and are studied by both botanists and zoologists because their vegetative phase of growth is animal-like while their reproductive phase is plant-like.

Slime molds are usually separated into two main groups. In one group, called the *cellular slime molds,* the vegetative phase consists of uninucleate, nonflagellate, free-living cells. Organisms in the second group are known as the *plasmodial slime molds.* In these, the vegetative phase consists of a multi-nucleate mass of protoplasm. Examples of both groups follow.

### Plasmodial Slime Molds

Plasmodial slime molds are common organisms in damp woods, where they may be found by stripping bark off fallen, partially rotted logs or by searching under leaf litter. They may also be found in soil, in gardens, and on lawns. Because of their small size and their manner of vegetative growth, they are not usually noticed.

The main vegetative phase of plasmodial slime molds consists of a multinucleate mass of protoplasm called a *plasmodium* (Fig. 4-1). It is from the general appearance of the plasmodium that the name "slime mold" originated. As the plasmodium moves slowly over the substrate, it engulfs and ingests solid food particles such as bacteria, yeast, and fungal spores. Nuclear division

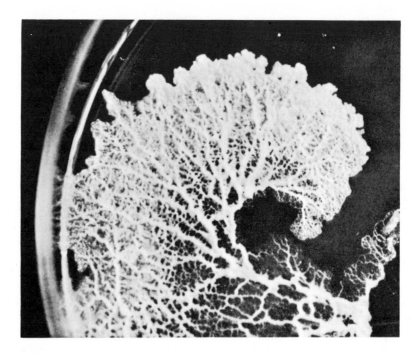

**Figure 4-1.** Plasmodium of *Physarum gyrosum* in agar culture. The interconnected system of protoplasmic tubules is evident. Courtesy of Dr. C. J. Alexopoulos, University of Texas, Austin.

is essentially synchronous; that is, all nuclei in a plasmodium undergo division at the same time. As nuclei enter prophase in *Physarum polycephalum,* the plasmodium stops locomotion and contracts slightly. Locomotion resumes immediately at telophase. As it does in many fungi, the nuclear membrane persists during mitosis; the spindle fibers are clearly intranuclear (Fig. 4-2).

The plasmodium of many slime molds is white; others may contain yellow, orange, or red pigments. The functions of these pigments are poorly understood. They are not photosynthetic. One suggestion is that yellow (and presumably other) pigmented types are more resistant to radiation than are unpigmented ones. In some cases, coloration is due to the ingestion of pigmented bacteria.

The plasmodium of slime molds lacks any type of a rigid wall. At the front end, where the plasmodium continually comes in contact with new substrate, the undifferentiated protoplasm is separated from the external environment by only a very thin membrane. In older parts of the plasmodium, the protoplasm is differentiated into an interconnected system of tubules that contain streaming cytoplasm. The tubules apparently are protoplasmic in nature and are capable of contraction and expansion. Cytoplasmic streaming in the tubules is easy to observe; for this reason, slime molds have long been studied by elementary students. We are not yet certain of the cause of cytoplasmic streaming. A contractile protein, myxomyosin, similar to the contractile protein actomyosin of animal muscle, has been isolated from slime-mold plasmodia. This protein contracts when the high-energy phosphate compound ATP is added, and it has been suggested that periodic contraction of myxomyosin causes cytoplasm to be moved passively through the tubules.

Under alternating day-night conditions, plasmodial growth continues as long as an adequate food supply and moisture are available. When either of these two factors limits growth, there is a rapid formation of reproductive structures. Experiments have shown that in *Physarum polycephalum* and many other slime molds, light (especially the shorter wavelengths) is necessary for initiation of reproduction; plasmodia grown in darkness do not form reproductive structures.

The reproductive structures of slime molds are referred to as fruiting bodies, of which the most common type is the sporangium (Fig. 4-3a, b). During sporangial formation, the plasmodium separates into many small mounds of protoplasm, each of which develops into a mature sporangium borne at the tip of a short stalk. During later stages in sporangium maturation, cleavage of the multinucleate protoplasm results in the formation of uninucleate spores. Each spore then develops a rigid wall. Judging from available evidence, meiosis occurs shortly before spore formation. Spores of slime molds, then, may have two important functions: they provide for the survival of the organism during periods unfavorable for vegetative growth, and they may contain new gene combinations resulting from segregation of genetic factors during meiosis.

At maturity, the surface layer of the sporangium flakes off, exposing the spore mass. Filamentous strands, which may help regulate spore dispersal, are usually intermixed with the spores. Spores are small and light and are blown about by the wind. Under favorable conditions, spores germinate and give rise to uninucleate flagellated cells. Usually, two whiplash flagella of unequal length are on the anterior end of each cell (Fig. 4-3c). These cells divide mitotically to form additional flagellated cells. Sometimes cells lose their flagella and move about like protozoan amoebae. Ultimately, two flagellated or nonflagellated cells fuse (*syngamy*) to initiate the plasmodium. Fusion results in the establishment of the diploid condition. The amoeboid cells, then, are haploid. There is

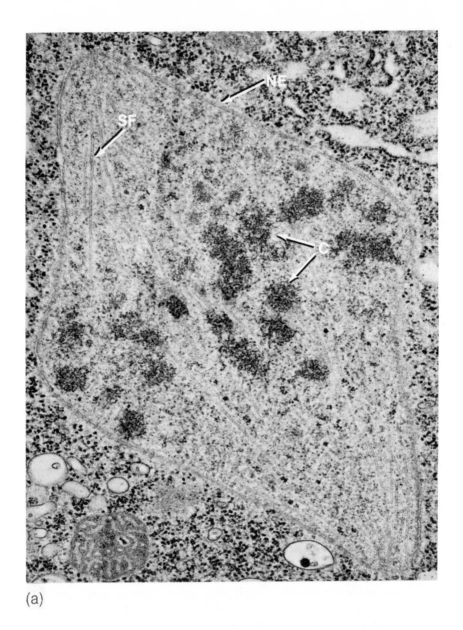

(a)

**Figure 4-2.** Mitosis in the plasmodium of *Physarum flavicomum,* showing the intranuclear spindle. (a) Metaphase. The nuclear envelope (NE) remains intact, the chromosomes (C) are aligned, and the spindle fibers (SF) are apparent. (b) Telophase. Note constriction of the nuclear envelope, the mass of chromatin (C) at the poles, and the persistence of the spindle fibers. Courtesy of Dr. H. C. Aldrich, University of Florida, Gainesville; from H. C. Aldrich, *Amer. J. Bot.* 56:290–299 (1969).

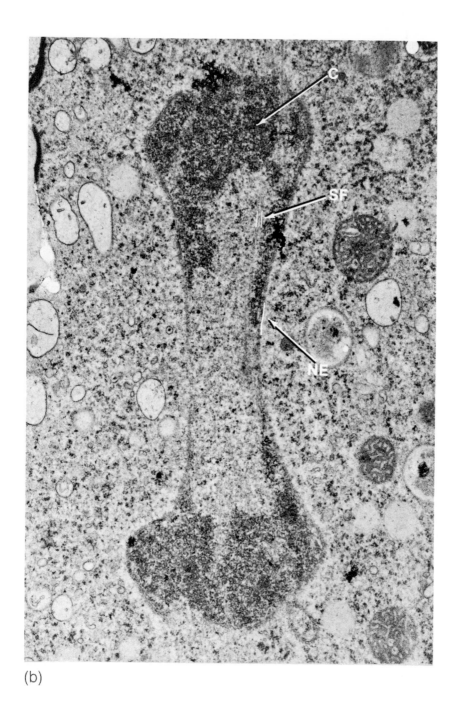

(b)

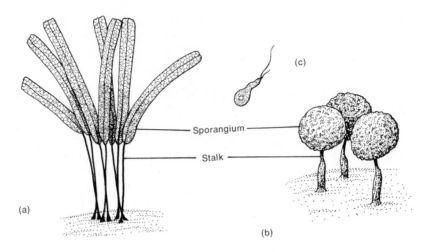

**Figure 4-3.** Sporangia and swarmer of plasmodial slime molds. (a) Sporangia of *Stemonitis*. (b) Sporangia of *Physarum*. (c) Biflagellate swarmer of a plasmodial slime mold. Figures not drawn to scale.

an interesting, and as yet unexplained, difference in nuclear behavior in the haploid amoebae and the diploid plasmodium. As mentioned earlier, the mitotic spindle is intranuclear in the plasmodium. On the other hand, the nuclear membrane breaks down and the spindle is extranuclear in the haploid amoebae. This is an unexpected change in organelle behavior resulting from the transition from haploidy to diploidy. The nature of this change as well as other (physiological) changes awaits further study.

Subsequent plasmodial growth occurs mainly by protein synthesis and concomitant nuclear divisions. During movement across the substrate, it is possible for a plasmodium to separate into several smaller ones, each capable of continued growth and reproduction. It is also possible for individual plasmodia of the same species to fuse with each other.

This account of slime mold development, although serving as a general introduction to these organisms, does not introduce the student to the many interesting unsolved problems in the group. For example, one of the most important aspects in slime mold development is the apparent absolute dependency of plasmodium formation on cell fusion. In 1958 it was found that the addition of chelating agents to cultures of young flagellated cells inhibited both cell fusion and plasmodium formation. The flagellated cells continued to divide as long as food (bacteria) was available, but they did not fuse. Only when these cells were transferred to a medium lacking chelating agents were plasmodia initiated. We still do not know the specific role of these agents: what metal ions are being chelated, or how the plasma membrane is altered. The mechanism by which cell fusion triggers plasmodium formation, and what biochemical differences exist between the free-living cells and the plasmodium, are other critical questions.

The vegetative plasmodial phase containing synchronously dividing nuclei has made the slime molds excellent organisms for cytological and biochemical research. It is now possible to grow *Physarum polycephalum* in a chemically defined liquid medium. In addition, the complete separation of vegetative growth from reproduction can be controlled by the investigator. Moreover, the large plasmodial size makes possible the sequential sampling of protoplasm during studies of biochemical changes correlated with morphological changes during sporulation. Removal of bits of protoplasm does not at all affect the metabolism of the rest of the plasmodium. Synchronous nuclear divisions also make possible the analysis of protein and nucleic acid synthesis, enzymatic changes, and other events during various stages of the nuclear division cycle.

### Cellular Slime Molds

The cellular slime molds are widely distributed soil-inhabiting organisms, but they are rarely seen except in the laboratory. This is because in their feeding phase the cellular slime molds exist as nonflagellated uninucleate cells, and their reproductive structures are quite small and ephemeral. Improvements in techniques to isolate and culture the cellular slime molds in recent years have led to the identification and study of an increasing number of these interesting organisms. Much of our information comes from studies on *Dictyostelium discoideum* (Fig. 4–4). The following account refers specifically to this species.

In contrast to the plasmodial slime molds in which the main vegetative phase is initiated by fusion of amoebae, the vegetative growth phase of the cellular slime molds consists entirely of individual, free-living amoebae. The uninucleate cells move about the substrate engulfing bacteria and are indistinguishable in form and behavior from protozoan amoebae. Cell multiplication is rapid when food is plentiful. An increased population above a certain minimum density or a diminution in food supply leads to changed behavior in the amoebae. Certain cells stop feeding and begin secreting a hormone-like substance called *acrasin*. Adjacent amoebae are attracted by acrasin and move toward these initial cells. These cells, in turn, begin to secrete acrasin and in this manner more and more amoebae are attracted toward the centers of aggregation. The amoebae are thus attracted over an increasingly wider area, and they move toward the centers in several broad streams. The heretofore free cells adhere to each other upon contact, forming a conical mound in the aggregation center.

Cells retain their individuality in the center of aggregation, and the resulting mass of cells, therefore, is called a *pseudoplasmodium* (pseudo = false). The

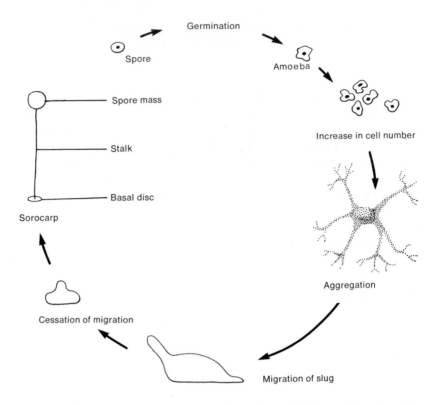

**Figure 4-4.** Stages in the life cycle of the cellular slime mold *Dictyostelium discoideum.*

pseudoplasmodium of *Dictyostelium discoideum* is called a slug because it is encased in a slimy sheath, it moves around the substrate prior to sporulation, and it leaves a slime trail in its wake. (The pseudoplasmodia of most cellular slime molds do not migrate; sporulation occurs at the sites of aggregation.) Movement of the slug is not a feeding response; the individual amoebae do not feed once aggregation has begun, and the slug as an "organism" lacks a mouth. The slug moves as an integrated unit, always with a particular end first, and it reacts to stimuli, often following light and temperature gradients. The pseudoplasmodium, however, is a relatively loose community of cells and can be readily dissociated by mechanical agitation without harm to the component cells.

At the time of sporulation, migration of the slug ceases and the tip of the slug rises upwards. The cells at the tip then move down through the center of the slug until they reach the substrate, forming a thin rod of differentiating cells through the center of the slug. This rod is the forerunner of the stalk of the mature reproductive structure. Cells of the stalk become vacuolate and, before dying, they secrete a cellulose sheath that gives structural rigidity to the stalk. The slug then moves up the stalk, and as it does new cells are added to the stalk apex. Thus the slug literally pulls itself up the stalk.

The amoebae that do not take part in stalk formation eventually form a globular mass at the apex of the stalk. Each cell then secretes a thin cellulose wall and becomes a spore. This delicate, ephemeral reproductive structure is called a *sorocarp* (soros = heap; karpos = fruit) (Fig. 4-4). Variation in sorocarp morphology is the main basis of classification of the cellular slime molds.

The occurrence of sexuality in the cellular slime molds is still not certain. Some scientists have reported evidence of its presence (for example, there is evidence that recombination occurs); others are not convinced by the evidence.

Part of the interest in cellular slime molds as research organisms is due to their change from the free-living state to one of simple multicellularity. With multicellularity come many of the attributes of more highly complex multicellular systems, including cell adhesion, interaction, and specialization. The nature of these interactions is of interest to morphogeneticists. The aggregation stage has been compared to the morphogenetic movement of cells that occurs during animal embryogenesis. Of particular interest are the factors that initiate cell movement in embryos, guide their movement, and determine where the cells finally settle down. The cells in animals, like those of the cellular slime molds, move as independent units, often by amoeboid movement, and adhere to each other when they arrive at their correct destination. Whether initial cell movement in animals is random or is chemically directed (as it is in cellular slime molds) is still unclear.

With multicellularity comes the cell interaction that leads to cell specialization and division of labor. The slug of *Dictyostelium discoideum* is differentiated into cells of three functional types. At the anterior end are those cells that give rise to most of the stalk of the sorocarp. The potential sporogenous cells comprise the bulk of the slug. The cells at the very posterior end of the slug give rise to the basal disk. A cell's function is determined by the position of that cell in the slug. This, in turn, is dictated to a considerable extent by the time of arrival of each amoeba at the center of aggregation. Those arriving first form the anterior end of the slug; those arriving later form the central portion of the slug; and those arriving last form the posterior part of the slug.

Cell interaction is such that once the slug has differentiated, cells of similar function seem to know where they should be in relation both to each other and to other types of cells in the pseudoplasmodium. This is clearly shown by the following kind of experiment. A vital stain (a type of stain that a cell takes up without injury to itself) is used to color a slug. The anterior end of this slug is then grafted near the posterior end of an unstained slug. Because of the color, the fate of the grafted cells can be followed visually. In this case, the colored cells migrate through the slug and come to take their place in their normal position at the anterior end, which now contains a mixture of stained and unstained cells (Fig. 4-5a). How do these cells perceive that they are in the wrong place and know in which direction to move? How are these cells different so that they begin their migration while cells normally in the posterior region do not? These are unanswered questions of considerable significance to the more general problem of morphogenetic movement of cells in animal development.

What happens when the slug is cut transversely in half? Do both parts develop complete sorocarps with stalks? The answer is yes; complete, but smaller, sorocarps develop (Fig. 4-5b). Loss of the anterior end apparently is perceived by the remaining cells and this is followed by re-establishment of new polarity in the slug with concomitant division of labor. (Additional information about the cellular slime molds can be obtained in Bonner's interesting book, listed in the Suggestions for Further Reading.)

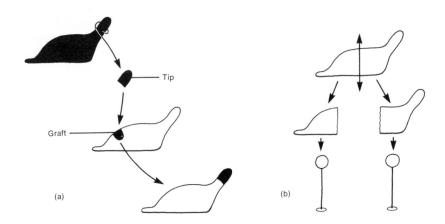

**Figure 4-5.** (a) Grafting experiment that shows that cell specialization has occurred in the slug of *Dictyostelium*. Cells in the tip of the black slug, when grafted to the posterior end of the white slug, migrate to the anterior end, their "correct" position, where they become mixed with the other cells at the anterior end of the slug. (b) An experiment that shows that cells in the slug retain the ability to dedifferentiate and redifferentiate, leading to the establishment of new polarity in the slug. The posterior half of the bisected slug regenerates a new anterior end and a normal, but smaller, sorocarp develops.

### Summary

| Group | Flagella | Vegetative Characteristics |
|---|---|---|
| Plasmodial | One or two whiplash | Plasmodial; multinucleate |
| Cellular | None | Cellular; uninucleate |

*Additional:* eukaryotic cellular structure; naked protoplasm (no cell walls); ingestion of solid food particles.

Chapter 4

### Evolutionary Relationships

The cellular slime molds are not obviously closely related either to the plasmodial slime molds or to the other organisms discussed in this book. They resemble the plasmodial slime molds primarily in that both lack cell walls and photosynthetic pigments. The cellular slime molds appear to be more closely related to the amoebae of the protozoa, and are here considered along with the plasmodial slime molds only for convenience.

The plasmodial slime molds have several attributes (including flagellar details [compare Fig. 3-2c, page 34 with Fig. 4-3c] and possession of multi-nucleate plasmodial vegetative growth phases) in common with one group of fungi (the Plasmodiophoromycetes, a class not discussed in this volume). Moreover, the details of sporangial development and the manner of spore development is reminiscent of fungi. This type of information has led some students of the plasmodial slime molds to conclude that these organisms represent early offshoots during the evolution of the fungi.

Other students, however, argue that the plasmodial slime molds have an affinity to the protozoa, and classify them with the amoeboid (rhizopod) organisms of this animal group. They argue that these slime molds evolved from amoeboid protozoa-like organisms. In this regard, it is of interest that some of the amoeboid protozoa appear to have evolved from certain photosynthetic chrysophycean- and xanthophycean-like ancestors, considered to be algae by botanists. (As will be shown later, loss of photosynthetic function by some algae is not impossible.) In view of the uncertain evolutionary relationships, it seems best to keep the plasmodial slime molds in a separate division, the Myxomycota, until more information becomes available and until other problems in protozoan, algal, and fungal phylogeny have been resolved.

# 5

## Introduction
## to Algae

Although the term "algae" does not enjoy formal taxonomic recognition, it is in wide general use and is familiar to most people. Basically, algae are photosynthetic, nonembryo-producing plants. (An embryo is here considered to be a multicellular young plant produced from the zygote and developed within the female reproductive structure.) As indicated in Chapter 1, algae do not form a natural group, but are subdivided into several divisions. It is of interest to note that the common names of most algal divisions refer to a color, such as red, green, blue-green, or brown. This color is characteristic of algae within a division and is due to the presence and different proportions of pigments in the cells.

Most algae are aquatic plants; they are the grass of the waters. The majority of free-floating and attached plants in both salt and fresh water are algae, and they may be abundant enough to color the water. The Red Sea reputedly derived its name from the occasional tremendous growths of a microscopic red-colored alga (which is a member of the blue-green algae division). Many others are soil algae and grow either in or on the surface of damp soil, where they are subjected to periodic drying. Relatively few algae are capable of surviving as epiphytes on the trunks and branches of trees. The truly subaerial algae, however, are able to survive rapid temperature fluctuations, temperature extremes, and long periods of dryness.

Although most algae are free-living, some occur in symbiotic associations with other organisms. Lichens—associations of fungi with either green or blue-green algae—have already been described. Some algae also live in close association with animals. One species of *Paramecium* (a unicellular protozoan) contains in its cytoplasm photosynthetic cells of a green alga; another green alga grows within the tissue of certain *Hydra* (a coelenterate). A few algae are even parasitic. Certain flowering plants are parasitized by green algae, and a few red algae are parasitic on close red algal relatives.

Since algae are predominantly aquatic plants, they are found in practically all bodies of water used by man, where they are often troublesome. Many communities obtain water from rivers, streams, lakes, ponds, or reservoirs, and algal growths in these bodies of water, and in swimming pools, may become extremely rapid at certain times of the year, producing "algal blooms" (Fig. 5-1). Not only do many of these algae impart fishy, musty, septic, grassy, or other disagreeable odors to our drinking water, but they may clog filters of water filtration plants. In smaller bodies of water, copper sulfate is often added to control algal growth, but the concentrations needed to kill all undesirable algae also kill other forms of aquatic life. In addition, it is usually not desirable to kill all algae in water, because they help keep water aerobic and tend to reduce water hardness. The synthesis and application of selective algicides

**Figure 5-1.**   Algal bloom in a small body of water.

(chemical compounds that inhibit the growth of specific undesirable algae in bodies of water) is an area of current research.

On the other hand, growths of large quantities of algae in sewage-disposal ponds has been encouraged. For many years, sanitary engineers have observed massive growths of green algae such as species of *Chlorella, Chlamydomonas,* and *Scenedesmus* (Fig. 5-2), in addition to bacteria, in sewage-treatment tanks

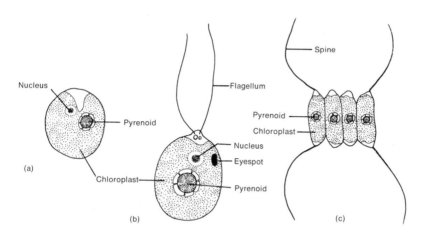

**Figure 5-2.** Common algae of sewage-treatment tanks. (a) *Chlorella.* (b) *Chlamydomonas.* (c) *Scenedesmus.*

and filter beds. Only after extensive research has the relationship that exists between these sewage algae and bacteria become apparent. It has been found that aerobic bacterial breakdown products of sewage are also primary photosynthetic requirements for these algae. Also, oxygen produced by algae can be an effective and inexpensive means of meeting the oxygen needs of aerobic sewage bacteria and thus prevent putrefaction. Slightly acidic raw sewage enters the pond at one end and is immediately acted upon by bacteria. The large amount of organic matter supports a very large bacterial population in this region of the pond, and sewage breakdown is rapid. Sewage input is a continuous process and, as the partially treated sewage moves slowly through the pond, the algal population, initially small, increases. As the algae utilize the nitrates, phosphates, and carbon dioxide made available by bacterial activity, the sewage becomes more and more alkaline. This alkaline condition inhibits most sewage bacteria so that in the discharged, treated sewage there is a low bacterial population and a high algal one (Fig. 5-3). Various modifications of this pond have been used in sewage treatment in several communities.

The large number of nutrients tied up in the algal protoplasts are discharged

---

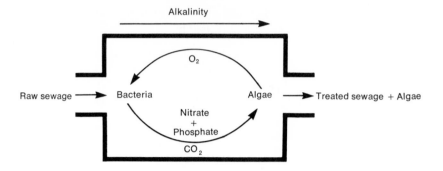

**Figure 5-3.**  Algal-bacterial interrelationship in a sewage-treatment tank.

along with the treated sewage-pond effluent. Several investigators have been interested in the possibility of harvesting these algae for animal food. These scientists are trying to find techniques of harvesting the algae and establishing suitable algae in sewage ponds. A similar, but closed, ecological system is under investigation for possible use in space travel. Algal and bacterial interaction under controlled conditions might solve the problems of sewage disposal, air rejuvenation, and water recycling during long-range space explorations. Algae, in turn, could be harvested periodically and used as food.

A considerable amount of research has also been directed toward the mass culturing of algae to meet the future food needs of man. In terms of available space for plant culture, the physical resources of our planet are drastically limiting; it is known that on a dry-weight basis algal culture is a more efficient utilization of space than either crop plants or meat animals. In this connection, much research has been done on various strains of the green alga *Chlorella* regarding their growth rates and nutritional value.

Because of their small size and ease of culture under carefully controlled conditions, algae have also been important organisms in research on photosynthetic processes. For example, much of our knowledge regarding the pathway of carbon during photosynthesis (see Jensen, *The Plant Cell,* this series) has been obtained from studies on algae, primarily green algae. The importance of photosynthesis cannot be overemphasized. Photosynthesis not only results in the liberation of molecular oxygen, which is essential for aerobic respiration, but it is also the most efficient system known by which radiant energy is converted to chemical energy. Although the pathway of carbon during photosynthesis is now quite well known, we still have much to learn about the energy-trapping mechanism itself. For example, how is radiant energy from the sun trapped by chlorophyll and other pigment molecules in chloroplasts? How are electrons transferred from molecule to molecule during this and other cellular processes? Algae (and photosynthetic bacteria as well) will no doubt continue to be important research organisms in these studies. Current and future research in the area of energy-trapping and electron-transfer systems is conducted at the level of submolecular biology. Needless to say, the influence of chemistry and physics on this level of biological research has been tremendous. But we must not lose sight of the fact that biology is more than a series of test-tube reactions, and any information obtained from isolated systems must be put back into its proper biological framework: that of the living, metabolizing cell and organism.

One of the most common overgeneralizations in regard to algae is that because they are photosynthetic, algae require only inorganic compounds — water, carbon dioxide, and light — for growth. While this is true for some (especially green algae), many algae also need one or more specific organic compounds for growth. For example, vitamin $B_{12}$ (which is also needed by animals and humans) is often required. Actually, the nutritional requirements of few algae have been critically studied, and there are many that we have not yet been able to culture. Although it might seem reasonable to assume that algae cultured in the dark would be able to grow if the medium were supplemented with a sugar normally present in light-grown cells, many algae fail to grow under such conditions. Some of these algae appear to have an obligate requirement for light; for a reason we have not yet determined, they are unable to utilize any externally supplied carbon source in the dark. Additional studies are needed on the basic biochemistry, physiology, and reproduction of more algae.

**Form of Algae**

Algae range in size from microscopic, unicellular plants to the highly differentiated, multicellular seaweeds that may be over 60 meters long. Unicellular algae are found in all divisions of algae with only one exception (brown algae), and are considered to be basic cell types from which, through evolution, other forms of body construction developed. Unicellular algae may be propelled through water by means of one or more flagella (Fig. 5-4), or they may be nonflagellated, and they may or may not have a rigid carbohydrate cell wall. Colonial algae are organisms in which daughter cells do not separate. Their association may be loose, as in the blue-green alga *Gloeocapsa* (Fig. 5-5a), or integrated, as in the green alga *Volvox* (Fig. 5-5b, c), in which individual cells are interconnected by thin protoplasmic strands. Filamentous algae develop from single cells in which division occurs primarily in a single plane, and in which the resulting filament may be branched or unbranched (Fig. 5-5d, e). Membranous and more complex seaweeds also develop from single cells, but cell divisions occur in more than one plane (Fig. 5-5f, g). A few

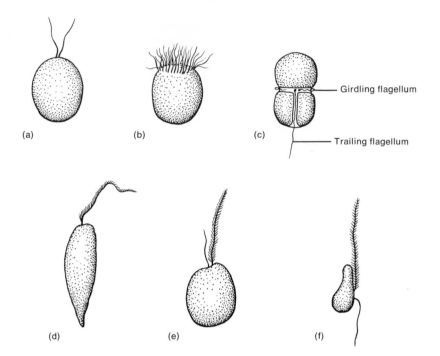

Girdling flagellum

Trailing flagellum

(a)          (b)          (c)

(d)          (e)          (f)

**Figure 5-4.**    Some types of flagellar arrangements in algae. (a) *Chlamydomonas* (a green alga). (b) Mitospore of *Oedogonium* (a green alga). (c) *Gymnodinium* (a dinoflagellate, one of a group of algae not discussed in this book). (d) *Euglena* (a euglenoid). (e) *Ochromonas* (a golden alga). (f) Sperm of *Laminaria* (a brown alga).

algae consist of nonseptate, branched, multinucleate tubes. In these algae, nuclear division occurs without accompanying cell division.

There is considerable diversity in form among unicellular and colonial algae. Many of these algae are planktonic organisms and possess flattened cells, cellular processes, or other flotation devices to keep the plants near the water surface, where light intensity is optimal. (Plankton are small, free-living plants and animals readily carried about by currents and found in almost all bodies of water. The plants are referred to as *phytoplankton;* the animals, as *zooplankton.*) Planktonic algae are the beginning point of many food chains. These microscopic plants are eaten by progressively larger organisms, including fish which in turn may be eaten by man:

phytoplankton → zooplankton → small fish → large fish → man.

The best fishing areas in the world are those high in plankton. It has been found that the addition of nitrates and other inorganic compounds to small bodies of water that are deficient in these compounds usually results in an

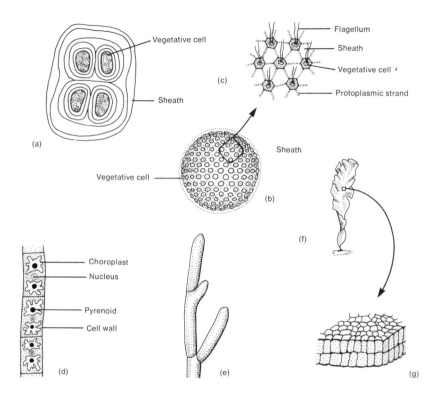

**Figure 5-5.** Common algal body forms. (a) Small colony of *Gloeocapsa* (a blue-green alga). (b) Low-power view of a colony of *Volvox* (a green alga). (c) High-power view of *Volvox*. (d) Unbranched filament of *Zygnema* (a green alga). (e) Branched filament of *Cladophora* (a green alga). (f) Habit drawing of the multicellular *Ulva* (a green alga). (g) High-power view of a portion of the plant of *Ulva*. Not drawn to scale.

increase both in algal growth and in fish productivity. Planktonic algae are also important in helping to maintain the carbon dioxide–oxygen ratio of the atmosphere. It has been estimated that about 70 per cent of photosynthesis occurs in oceans; most of this is accomplished by phytoplankton (about which we know very little).

Most larger algae are attached to the bottom in aquatic habitats. The largest and most complex are found in marine waters, where they are common inhabitants of the intertidal zone or deeper water. (The intertidal zone is defined as that area between the mean high tide and the mean low tide.) Although many of the algae are eaten by animals such as sea urchins, they are less important in food chains leading to man than are plankton algae. It should be mentioned, however, that the culturing and harvesting of certain attached red and brown marine algae is a flourishing food industry in several Asiatic countries, including China and Japan.

---

We have seen that the unicell is considered to be the basic cell type from which other body types have been derived. Although details of form and structure in the unicell differ in each algal division, there are many general similarities. Thus a description of the form and function of the flagellated unicell at this time will also serve as an introduction to the algal cell in general (Fig. 5-6).

Cells of most algae are surrounded by a primarily carbohydrate wall in which cellulose is almost always present. In addition, the walls of many algae contain a gelatinous material that is often pectinaceous. This material has various functions in algae; in colonial forms it holds the cells together, and in many subaerial algae it helps retard desiccation. Other carbohydrates obtained from the cell walls of several marine brown and red algae are of commercial importance and will be described in more detail later.

The chloroplast is the most prominent cell organelle. It is a complex structure containing a number of photosynthetic lamellae, and is separated from the cytoplasm by a double unit membrane (Fig. 5-6; 5-8). Careful study of electronmicrographs has shown that the lamellae are parts of closed, flattened sac-like structures. Each sac-like structure is called a *thylakoid*. In some algae (for example, the red algae) the thylakoids are free from each other, but in others (for example, the brown algae), the thylakoids are stacked for much of their length in groups of two or more (compare Fig. 5-7 with Fig. 5-8).

Many of the pigments and enzymes involved in photosynthesis are integral parts of the thylakoid membranes. As indicated in Chapter 1, several different kinds of chlorophyll molecules occur in algae. Chlorophyll *a* occurs in all photosynthetic algae and land plants, whereas the other chlorophylls occur in certain plant groups but not in others (see later). The chlorophylls, as well as *fucoxanthin* (a carotenoid pigment involved in photosynthesis in some algae; see later), occur in the thylakoid membranes. The blue and red *phycobiliproteins* of red and blue-green algae have been shown to occur in particles called *phycobilisomes* attached to the outer surface of the thylakoid membranes (Fig. 5-8). The phycobiliproteins and fucoxanthin, called accessory photosynthetic pigments, function to absorb light in the middle portion of the light spectrum, where chlorophyll absorption is low (Fig. 5-9). The absorbed energy participates in photosynthesis, apparently by transferral of the energy to chlorophyll *a*. The efficiency of energy transfer is very high, often better than 90 per cent. A more direct involvement in photosynthesis has been suggested for fucoxanthin.

The occurrence of fucoxanthin and phycobiliproteins in predominantly aquatic algae is significant in relation to algal distribution. Because water filters out much red light, these pigments absorb strongly those wavelengths with higher transmission (especially in sea water). The accessory pigments thus serve to fill the absorption gap of chlorophyll and most likely enable organisms to grow in habitats otherwise unsuitable. Laboratory experiments on blue-green algae have shown that for some, but not all, of these algae a change in light wavelength is followed by a corresponding and reversible change in the proportions

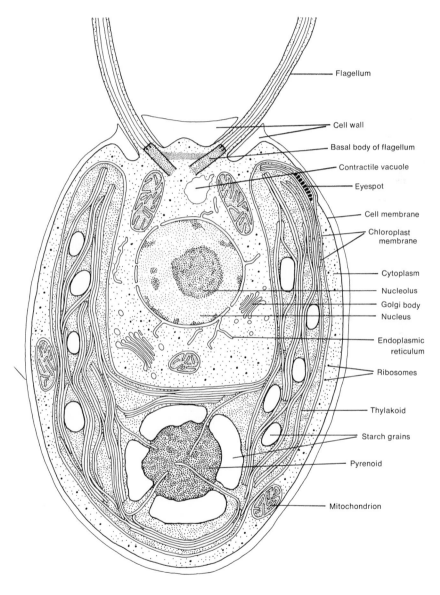

**Figure 5-6.** Diagrammatic representation of the cell structure of *Chlamydomonas*, a unicellular green alga. Reconstructed from several electronmicrographs published by different authors.

---

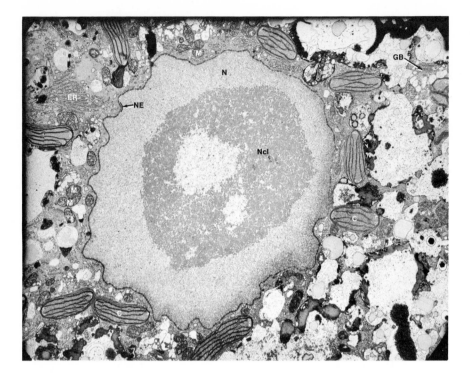

**Figure 5-7.** Apical cell of *Zonaria*, a multicellular brown alga. All of the major features of a eukaryotic cell are visible: nuclear envelope (NE) with nuclear pores; nucleus (N); nucleolus (Nu); chloroplasts (C) with stacked thylakoids; mitochondria (M); Golgi bodies (GB); and an endoplasmic reticulum (ER). Courtesy of Dr. M. Neushul, University of California, Santa Barbara.

of blue and red phycobiliproteins in the cell. The change in pigmentation is toward facilitating maximum utilization of available incident energy. This type of wavelength-induced change in cell pigmentation has been termed *chromatic adaptation*.

Chloroplasts of many algae contain one or more specialized proteinaceous areas called *pyrenoids* (Fig. 5-6). Pyrenoids in green algae are associated with starch synthesis; in these algae, and in other green plants, starch always forms within chloroplasts (or their colorless counterparts). Pyrenoids are found in the chloroplasts of many algae in other divisions. In these algae, however, careful studies with the electron microscope have indicated that polysaccharide food reserve is synthesized externally to the chloroplast, in the cytoplasm, sometimes far removed from the vicinity of a pyrenoid. The function of the pyrenoid in these algae is unknown.

Motility is due to the activity of one or more (usually two) flagella that are

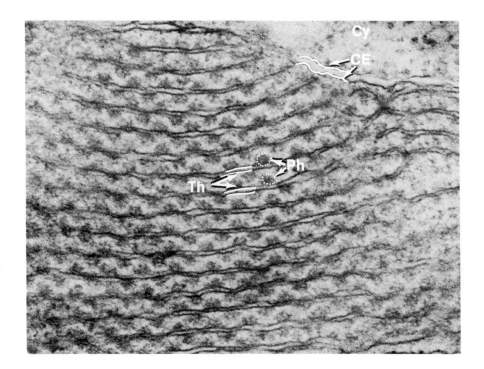

**Figure 5-8.** Details of chloroplast structure of the unicellular red alga, *Porphyridium cruentum*. Note the parallel arrangement of the thylakoids (Th), the attachment of the phycobilisomes (Ph) to the thylakoids, the double unit membrane of the chloroplast envelope (CE), and the cytoplasm (Cy) of the cell. Courtesy of Dr. E. Gantt, Smithsonian Institution; from E. Gantt and S. F. Conti, *J. Cell Biol.*, 29:423–434 (1966).

laterally or anteriorly inserted (Fig. 5-6). Each flagellum arises from a basal granule within the cytoplasm and extends through a pore in the cell wall to the outside. Characteristically, green algae have two whiplash flagella, euglenoids have one (or more) tinsel flagella, and brown algae have one of each type. The flagellum is an organelle for locomotion. Although several different patterns of flagellar motion have been described in algae, we still know little about the biophysics of flagellar contraction, or how impulses are transmitted along the length of the flagellum. Many unicellular algae lack flagella. In some cases, this appears to be a derived condition. It is known that mutants of flagellated cells showing a permanent loss of flagella can be induced to arise in the laboratory, and such mutants probably also occur in nature. It is possible that the nonflagellated green alga *Chlorella* evolved from a flagellated ancestor.

Flagellated cells of many algae are capable of reacting to variations in light intensity; they may swim toward or away from a light source, depending on its intensity (positive and negative phototaxis, respectively). In order to react, cells must absorb light. Many flagellated cells possess an eyespot (stigma) —

---

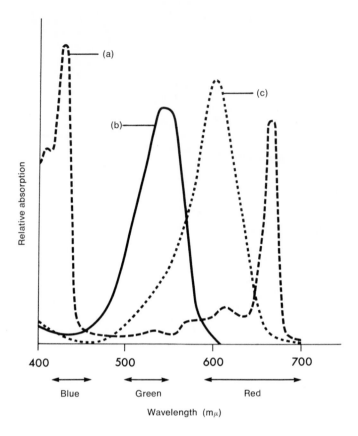

**Figure 5-9.** Absorption spectra of a few photosynthetic pigments. (a) chlorophyll *a;* (b) phycoerythrin; (c) phycocyanin. The two phycobiliproteins tend to close the photosynthetic window of chlorophyll *a.*

generally a modified part of the chloroplast — which contains a red or orange carotenoid pigment (Fig. 5-6). The eyespot is involved in the phototactic responses of many algae, but the mechanism of its involvement has been shown in only one organism (*Euglena*).

In addition, cells of most flagellated fresh-water algae also contain one or more contractile vacuoles that function as osmotic regulators. In fresh water, the concentration of dissolved substances within the cell is higher than in the surrounding water. Consequently, the water that tends to move into the cell is removed by the activity of these vacuoles.

The structure (Fig. 5-7) and function of mitochondria and nuclei of algae are similar to those of eukaryotic plants in general and need not be described in detail here. It is sufficient to recall that both of these structures are limited externally by a double unit membrane.

# 6

## Blue-Green Algae

Blue-green algae, or Cyanophyta (cyan = blue; phyton = plant), are found in a wide variety of environments. They occur in marine and fresh water, on and in soil, and on wet stones, cement, and plant pots. Some can withstand the temperatures of hot springs, others the cold of arctic pools. Still others are normal inhabitants of the alimentary canal of some animals, and another is an intracellular symbiont of an unicellular, flagellated, and otherwise colorless organism. Certain blue-green algae such as *Anabaena* are able to utilize elemental nitrogen from the atmosphere to build their proteins, thereby contributing to the nitrogenous content of soil. This process of nitrogen fixation, which is similar to that found in some bacteria, is important for maintaining soil fertility, for instance, in rice paddies.

Except for nitrogen fixation, blue-green algae are of little direct benefit to man. Some are common components of algal water blooms and occasionally have been implicated in the illness and death of mammals, waterfowl, fish, and man. Laboratory studies on cultures have shown that a few of the blue-green algae produce toxic compounds. Two factors that can cause death have been described in a species of the colonial *Microcystis* commonly found in toxic water blooms. One, called a fast-death factor, results in death in one to two hours, preceded by pallor, convulsions, and prostration. The fast-death factor, an endotoxin, is a polypeptide of ten amino acid residues.

**General Characteristics**

The cellular structure of blue-green algae is relatively simple (Fig. 6-1). Like those of bacteria, the cells of blue-green algae are prokaryotic; double unit membraned organelles, such as mitochondria, nuclei, and chloroplasts, are absent. The photosynthetic lamellae (called thylakoids) are located mainly in the cell periphery, although some traverse the cell center as well. Only one kind of chlorophyll, chlorophyll a, is found. In addition, the cells usually contain one or both of the colored phycobiliproteins (the red phycoerythrin and the

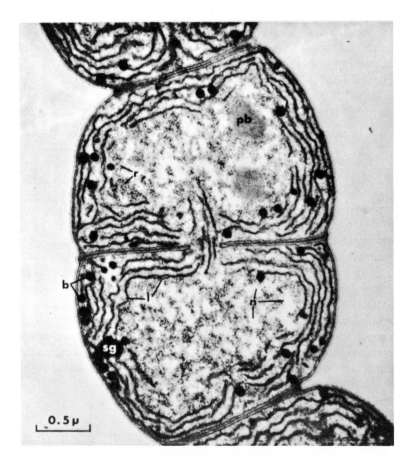

**Figure 6-1.** Electronmicrograph of *Nostoc punctiforme*. Note the absence of nuclear and chloroplast membranes and mitochondria. Septum formation is by the centripetal ingrowth of the new wall. Labelled in the cytoplasm are: granules (osmiophilic bodies) (b); photosynthetic membranes or thylakoids (l); DNA fibrils (n); polyhedral bodies (polyphosphate granules) (pb); structured granules (a proteinaceous food reserve) (sg); and ribosomes (r). Courtesy of Dr. T. E. Jensen and Dr. C. C. Bowen, Iowa State University, Ames.

blue phycocyanin). As pointed out in Chapter 5, the granules (phycobilisomes) containing the phycobiliproteins are closely associated with the thylakoids. The thylakoid membranes of blue-green algae are involved in more than photosynthesis. They appear to be functional mosaics containing, in addition to enzymes involved in photosynthesis, localized regions that bear chains of respiratory enzymes and (in nitrogen-fixing species) other regions that bear enzymes involved in nitrogen-fixation.

Excess sugar resulting from photosynthesis is stored as glycogen. (It is practically indistinguishable from animal glycogen.) The food reserve of blue-green algae was earlier given the name of cyanophycean starch, because it differs significantly from the starches of other algal groups. Now that its chemistry is reasonably well known, there seems no reason not to refer to it simply as glycogen. In many filamentous species, glycogen is closely associated with the crosswalls.

The color of blue-green algae may be other than blue-green. Purple, violet, red, yellow, or green algae may occur because of variations in the kinds and proportions of pigments, particularly phycobiliproteins. A few are colorless and thus nonphotosynthetic. The nonphotosynthetic forms closely resemble bacteria, but they are similar to blue-green algae in size, form, and manner of motility.

The nuclear material, which is not bounded by a membrane, is generally located in the central region of the cell. DNA is present, but chromosomes have not been identified; a normal mitotic division does not occur. The nuclear material is more or less equally divided during cell division. We do not yet understand how a complete set of genes is equally divided during division. Until 1962 (Kumar, *Nature*, 196:1121-1122), genetic evidence for the existence of sexuality in this algal division had not been found. However, apparent genetic recombination does occur in *Anacystis nidulans*, a colonial blue-green alga. Two strains of this alga were used for the study: one strain was resistant to penicillin but sensitive to streptomycin; the other was sensitive to penicillin but resistant to streptomycin. Cells of each strain were mixed together and cultured in a medium that lacked both antibiotics. Therefore neither strain's growth was inhibited. Subsequently, inocula were withdrawn and transferred to culture flasks containing both antibiotics. Growth occurred in a significant number of cultures. Since neither strain will grow separately under these conditions, it seems probable that growth resulted from the appearance of recombinant cells resistant to both antibiotics. In these studies, the number of recombinants (one in about 100 million cells of the parental population) was similar to that obtained during early study of bacterial sexuality. In addition, evidence for genetic recombination was reported in 1965 for a species of *Cylindrospermum*. However, these reports have been questioned and additional research is needed to indicate how widespread and important sexuality is in blue-green algae and the type(s) of genetic systems that are involved. If it occurs, it is probably similar to bacterial conjugation.

The blue-green algal cell lacks a large central aqueous vacuole and, as in bacteria, cell enlargement after division is due primarily to protein synthesis. The cytoplasm contains numerous ribosomes, but an endoplasmic reticulum is absent. In planktonic blue-green algae, a type of vacuole, called a *gas vacuole,* is found. The number and size of the vacuoles are variable. In some species they may disappear completely, and this is followed by a *de novo* origin of new ones. Young gas vacuoles are biconical organelles which increase in size apparently by the intercalation of new material near the center of the developing cylinder (Fig. 6-2). When gas vacuoles are present in sufficient size and number they cause the cells to float, and they thus play an

(a)

**Figure 6-2.** Gas vacuole formation in *Nostoc muscorum.* (a) Young gas vacuole 7 hours after induction. (b) Gas vacuoles 16 hours after induction. Arrows indicate possible place of addition of new components to the growing vacuole. Courtesy of Dr. J. R. Waaland and Dr. D. Branton, University of California, Berkeley; from J. R. Waaland and D. Branton, *Science,* 163:1339–1341 (1969).

important role in keeping these nonflagellated cells near the surface of bodies of water. Gas vacuoles are particularly abundant in the blue-green algae of "water blooms."

Cell walls, rigid sheaths, and gelatinous sheaths have been described for many species. Although cellulose, pectic substances, and several other compounds have been reported, the chemical composition, structure, and bio-

(b)

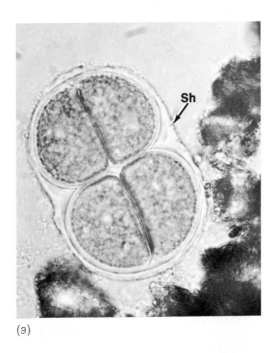

(a)

**Figure 6-3.** Blue-green algae. (a) *Chroococcus turgidus*. Note Sheath (Sh). (b) *Oscillatoria* sp. Note separation disc (SD). (c) *Anabaena* sp., with helical filaments and heterocysts (H).

synthesis of cell walls and sheaths of most of these algae are poorly known. Additional studies utilizing modern techniques are needed to fill this gap in our knowledge.

There are no flagellated cells, either vegetative or reproductive, in blue-green algae, and there is no evidence to indicate that these algae evolved from flagellated ancestors. In this division, the nonflagellated unicell is considered to be the basic cell type. Many blue-green algae such as *Gloeocapsa* (Fig. 5-5a, page 93) and *Chroococcus* (Fig. 6-3a) (organisms that may be found on damp terrestrial habitats like wet rocks and flower pots in greenhouses) are colonial; the individual cells are held together by a gelatinous sheath. In these forms, reproduction occurs simply by fragmentation of the parent colony. However, the commonest body form in this division is the filament, which may be branched or unbranched (Fig. 6-3b, c; 6-4).

There is usually little cell specialization along the filament. An exception is the *separation disc* (Fig. 6-3b) resulting from the death of an occasional cell along the filament in *Oscillatoria* and a few other genera. The separation disc aids vegetative reproduction (fragmentation) by forming weak places along the filament. In *Anabaena* and some other genera, specialized cells called *hetero-*

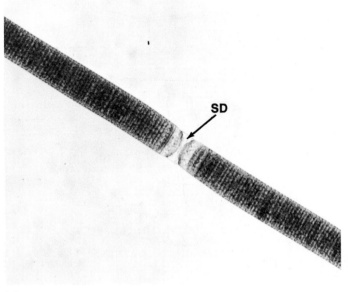

(b)

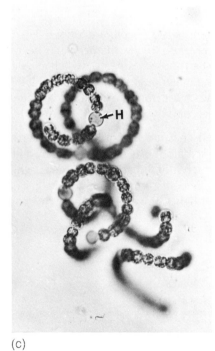

(c)

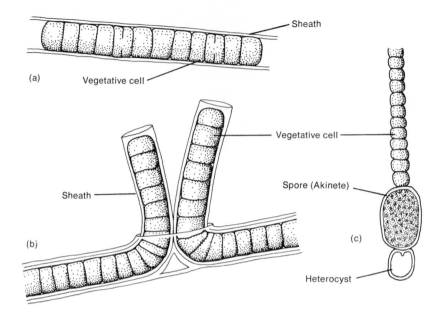

**Figure 6-4.** Filamentous blue-green algae. (a) *Lyngbya*, an *Oscillatoria*-like filament surrounded by a sheath. (b) *Scytonema*, showing branching. (c) *Cylindrospermum* with terminal heterocyst, subterminal akinete, and vegetative cells behind.

*cysts* (heteros = different; kystis = cell) are formed (Fig. 6-3c; 6-4c). Germination of heterocysts to give rise to new filaments has been confirmed. Relatively few species form resistant spores (*akinetes*), which are enlarged vegetative cells filled with food storage material and surrounded by a thick wall (Fig. 6-4c). In most blue-green algae, the cytoplasm itself is capable of withstanding long periods of unfavorable conditions.

Although flagellated cells are absent, many species are capable of movement. For example, *Oscillatoria* (Fig. 6-3b) moves by a gliding movement, and attached filaments, which are free at only one end, exhibit a slow, oscillating motion. Maximum movement in some blue-green algae is induced by radiation with red or blue-violet light. However, the basic mechanism for movement is not understood.

### Summary

| Photosynthetic Pigments | Flagella | Food Reserve |
| --- | --- | --- |
| Chlorophyll *a* Phycobiliproteins | None | Glycogen |

*Additional:* prokaryotic cellular organization (no nuclear, mitochondrial, or chloroplast double unit membranes); conjugation type of sexual reproduction?; amitosis.

**Evolutionary Relationships**

Blue-green algae are believed to represent primitive plants that have remained more or less at the evolutionary level at which they arose. There is fossil evidence of their antiquity. Filaments comparable to those of present-day, living *Oscillatoria* have been found in Precambrian rocks at least one and a half billion years old, and there is additional fossil evidence that the blue-green algae have a geologic age of some two to two and a half billion years.

In cellular structure (including cell wall composition), blue-green algae more closely resemble bacteria than other algae. Moreover, the few blue-green algal viruses known more closely resemble bacteriophages in their morphology than they do viruses of animals or higher plants. It is not surprising, then, that a close relationship between blue-green algae and bacteria has been postulated. According to this line of thought, blue-green algae either evolved from bacteria or had a common ancestry with bacteria. A logical consequence would be to place both blue-green algae and bacteria in the same division, and some biologists classify them in this manner.

Blue-green algae and bacteria, however, differ in a number of respects, such as types of chlorophyll pigments, types of accessory photosynthetic pigments, details of photosynthesis (there is a lack of oxygen evolution in bacteria), presence of flagella in photosynthetic bacteria, and manner of motility (the motility of nonflagellated bacteria is quite different from that of blue-green algae). Such differences lead me to conclude that blue-green algae do not have a close phylogenetic relationship with bacteria, but that these two groups are at the same evolutionary level of organization. They both have a prokaryotic organization because they evolved during the same early period of geologic time, when evolving cells were very simple. In this view, their present similarity in structure and function is explained by the geologic age of their origin rather than by a common ancestry. Organisms in both groups arose under similar ecological conditions, with similar precursor pools available in the surrounding environment.

# 7

## Red Algae

Red algae, or Rhodophyta (rhodon = rose; phyton = plant), are most commonly found along rocky stretches of seacoasts. Most of them grow in the lower part of the intertidal zone or in deeper water where they are not exposed to the full force of wave action. Red algae are found in all oceans but are more abundant in warm marine water. Although they are mostly marine, several fresh-water species are known. These usually grow in cold, swiftly-flowing streams. The red algae's color can be used to distinguish them from most other algae.

Some red algae are found in coral reefs, and studies on present-day reef formation in the Southern Hemisphere indicate that coralline red algae are more important in reef building than are coral animals. Fossil calcareous reefs give evidence of the existence of red algae as far back as 425 million years ago.

### General Characteristics

Red algae are relatively small plants. Most of them are less than 2 feet in length, but only a few are microscopic. *Porphyridium* (Fig. 7-1), which is found in both fresh and brackish water as well as on damp soil, is one of the few unicellular species known. Other plants vary from delicate membranous sheets (*Porphyra*) or simple branched filaments, to intricately branched, lacy types (Fig. 7-2). The plant body of many red algae, such as *Nemalion*, is composed

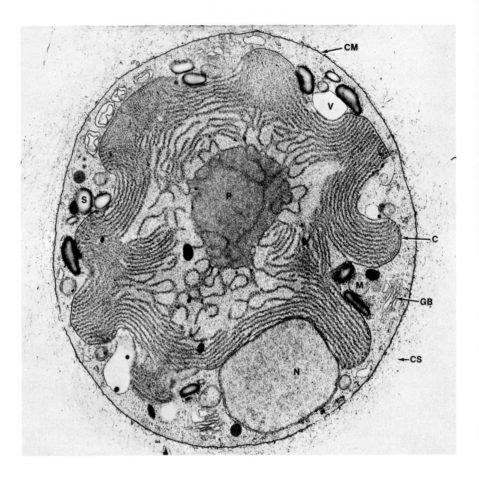

**Figure 7-1.** Cell structure of *Porphyridium cruentum*, a unicellular red alga. The cell is surrounded by a cell membrane (CM) and a diffuse carbohydrate sheath (CS). The large chloroplast (C) possesses a pyrenoid (P), but the floridean starch (S) occurs as granules scattered in the cytoplasm. Note the association of phycobilisomes with the thylakoids. Also visible is a nucleus (N), Golgi bodies (GB), mitochondria (M), and vacuoles (V). Courtesy of Dr. E. Gantt, Smithsonian Institution; from E. Gantt and S. F. Conti, *J. Cell Biol.*, 26:365–381 (1965).

of highly branched filaments. In these algae, one or more filaments of elongate cells form the axis of the plant; from these intertwined axial filaments arise numerous, highly branched lateral filaments. The lateral filaments are the main photosynthetic parts of the plants. The axial filaments are nearly colorless.

The cell structure of red algae is eukaryotic. Nuclei, mitochondria, and chloroplasts, all bounded by double unit membranes, are found. Golgi bodies and an endoplasmic reticulum also occur (Figs. 7-1; 7-3). Flagellated cells are

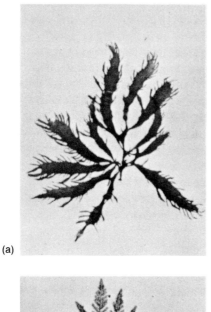

(a)

(b)

**Figure 7-2.** Examples of multicellular red algae. (a) *Farlowia.* (b) *Ptilota.*

unknown. The chloroplasts contain a number of thylakoids (flattened, sac-like structures) with associated phycobilisomes (granules that contain the blue and red phycobiliproteins). Chlorophyll *a* is present, and chlorophyll *d* has been isolated from less than half of the algae studied. The characteristic color of most red algae is due to the abundance of the phycobiliprotein, phycoerythrin.

The blue phycocyanin also occurs in many red algae, but usually in small amounts. Some red algae may be nearly green in color; others are nearly black.

Many elegant studies on light absorption by nonchlorophyll pigments have been carried out using red algae. These investigations have shown that, as in blue-green algae, light energy absorbed by phycobiliproteins participates in photosynthesis. The presence of phycobiliproteins undoubtedly influences the distribution of marine red algae. Many of these algae grow in deep water or in shaded areas where light intensity is relatively low. Accessory photosynthetic pigments such as phycobiliproteins absorb wavelengths of light not absorbed by chlorophyll, which, as pointed out in Chapter 5, results in a more efficient utilization of available light energy.

Excess photosynthate is stored as floridean starch. Although pyrenoids are present in the chloroplasts of some red algae, they do not appear to be involved in the synthesis of the food reserve. Floridean starch accumulates outside the chloroplast (Fig. 7-1), often far removed from the pyrenoid, and pyrenoid function in these algae (or in any algae, for that matter) is unknown.

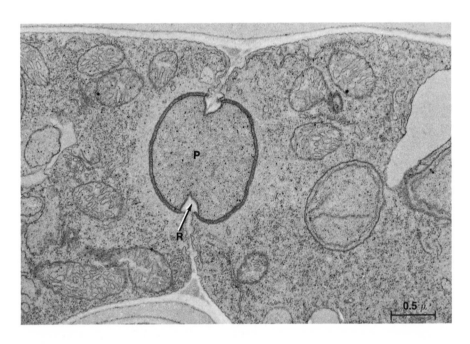

**Figure 7-3.** Pit connection of the red alga, *Pseudogloiophloea confusa*. Completed pit connection with rimmed aperture (r) closed by a highly structured plug (p). Courtesy of Dr. J. Ramus, Yale University, New Haven; from J. Ramus, *J. Phycol.* 5:57–63 (1969).

Cell division is by the centripetal ingrowth of a new wall from the cell periphery toward the cell center. Septation, however, is not usually complete. An aperture (or pore) remains, and the cell membrane is continuous between adjacent cells. Later, the aperture is generally closed by a rather highly structured plug (Fig. 7-3) that serves as a barrier and prevents cytoplasmic continuity. The septum, aperture, and plug combination is called a *pit connection*.

The cell is generally surrounded by a wall of two layers. The inner layer, next to the cell membrane, contains cellulose. The outer layer is mucilaginous, causing the slimy surface of many red algae. It contains colloidal substances and serves to prevent the rapid drying of intertidal red algae when they are exposed during low tide.

Considerable research is being done on the chemical composition of the cell wall in red algae, because the colloidal substances of some red algae have great economic importance. For example, *Gelidium* and a few other genera are the sources of agar, perhaps best known as a culture medium for bacteria and fungi. Agar has a number of additional uses. It has been used to retain moisture for long periods of time in fruit cakes, icings, frostings, pie fillings, cheeses, mayonnaise, salad dressings, tooth pastes, and shaving creams, and in cosmetics as a base for greaseless creams. Most commercial agar comes from Japan, but red algae have also been harvested for their agar content on the east and west coasts of North America. A few red algal species are also used in soups and as food flavorings. Pieces of *Porphyra*, a common plant of the upper intertidal zone, are used on cookies and crackers and in soups in the Orient. Some species of *Porphyra* have a cholesterol-splitting enzyme, and there is a report that people who eat *Porphyra* have a low incidence of heart disease.

There is considerable variation in detail in the processes of sexual reproduction in red algae, and use is made of this variation in classification. While a detailed description is beyond the scope of this book, a few general comments are necessary. Sexual reproduction is oogamous, which is considered to be an advanced condition. The male gametes are nonflagellate and are called *spermatia*. The female sex structure is called a *carpogonium* (karpos = fruit; gignesthai = to be born) and consists of a swollen base that contains the egg nucleus, and an elongate structure called a trichogyne (Fig. 7-4). When mature, spermatia are released and are passively carried by water currents; contact with a trichogyne occurs entirely by chance. Upon contact, fusion and dissolution of the cell walls at the point of contact is followed by migration of the male nucleus to the base of the carpogonium.

The details of the events that follow entry of the sperm nucleus into the base of the carpogonium are variable, and these details are widely used in classification of red algae. After fertilization, a cluster of short filaments, called a

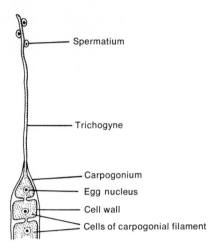

**Figure 7-4.** Portion of a carpogonial branch. Spermatia attach to the elongate trichogyne of the carpogonium.

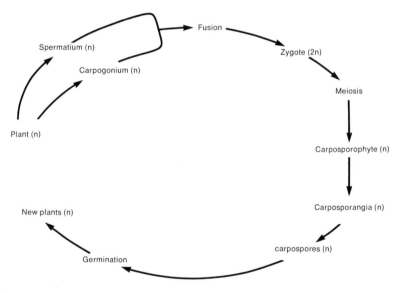

**Figure 7-5.** Life cycle of *Batrachospermum* and some species of *Nemalion*.

*carposporophyte,* develops. These filaments give rise to *carposporangia* which, in turn, give rise to *carpospores.* (Note that the carposporophyte develops on the same plant that bears the carpogonium; whether it develops directly from the carpogonium, or from another cell, depends upon the species.)

When meiosis occurs prior to carpospore formation, the carpospores are haploid and they give rise to new haploid plants upon spore germination. The fresh-water *Batrachospermum* and some species of the marine *Nemalion* exhibit this developmental pattern and their life cycle is diagrammed in Fig. 7-5.

Many red algae, on the other hand, develop diploid carpospores; meiosis does not occur until later in the life cycle. Upon germination, the diploid carpospores give rise to a free-living, diploid plant. Meiosis occurs in specific cells of this diploid plant. Since four spores develop in each cell that undergoes meiosis, the diploid plant is called a *tetrasporophyte.* In these plants, there is a free-living haploid plant, a parasitic diploid carposporophytic phase, and a free-living diploid plant in the life cycle. *Polysiphonia* (which has separate male and female haploid plants) has this developmental pattern and its life cycle is diagrammed in Fig. 7-6.

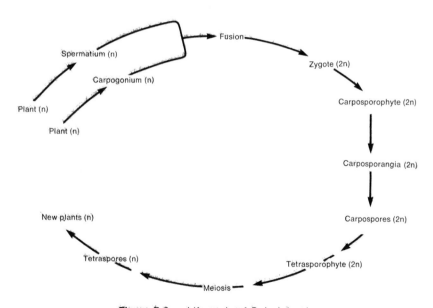

**Figure 7-6.**   Life cycle of *Polysiphonia.*

**Summary**

| Photosynthetic Pigments | Flagella | Food Reserve |
|---|---|---|
| Chlorophyll a | None | Floridean starch |
| ± Chlorophyll d | | |
| Phycobiliproteins | | |

*Additional*: eukaryotic cellular structure; oogamous sexual reproduction; details and processes following sexual reproduction usually complex; mostly marine plants.

**Evolutionary Relationships**

Red algae are a well-defined group. They resemble blue-green algae in being nonflagellated and in having phycobiliproteins. However, not all phycobiliproteins of these two groups are identical, and they are also found in other algae (for example, in members of the Cryptophyceae, a small group of flagellate algae not discussed in this book). With an increasing interest in the study of photosynthetic mechanisms in algae grown in culture, it is possible that we will find phycobiliproteins more widely distributed than now thought. At this time, we must be careful not to place too much weight on their possession of phycobiliproteins as an indication of close relationship.

The eukaryotic cellular structure of red algae can be used to argue against a close relationship between red and blue-green algae. All double-membrane structures present in red algal cells are absent in blue-green algae. This fact indicates a basic difference in the organization of biochemical pathways in these two algal divisions. Moreover, there is a great gap in the fossil record between the time of appearance of the earliest known blue-green algae (over 2 billion years) and red algae. Undoubted fossils of red algae occur from about the Cretaceous period and onward, although the existence of calcareous reefs in the Ordovician Period (some 425 million years ago) is circumstantial evidence for the simultaneous occurrence of red algae, but this interpretation has been questioned. I consider it doubtful that the red algae evolved from blue-green algae.

The development of a carposporophyte following fertilization perhaps is somewhat analogous to the postfertilization development of the ascogenous hyphae of the filamentous ascomycetes. Similarity in shape of the carpogonium, with its trichogyne, to the ascogonium is also noteworthy. (The possible relationship of red algae to the Ascomycetes was discussed in Chapter 3.)

## Chapter 7

# 8

## Golden Algae
## and Diatoms

The division Chrysophyta (chryso = golden; phyton = plant) includes unicellular and colonial planktonic algae of marine or fresh water. They play an important role in the economy of nature both as photosynthesizers and as the beginning of many food chains.

Chrysophytes have eukaryotic cellular structures. Chlorophyll *a* is the dominant green pigment, and excess food is stored either as the glucose polymer *chrysolaminarin* (leucosin), or as oils. In addition, cell walls and walls of resistant spores of many chrysophytes contain silica. The Chrysophyta is separated into two groups: golden algae (Chrysophyceae) and the diatoms (Bacillariophyceae). (The yellow-green algae were earlier placed in the Chrysophyta, but recent studies have further indicated the distinctness of these algae, and they are now usually placed in a separate division, the Xanthophyta. The yellow-green algae are a relatively small group of organisms, and they closely parallel the golden algae in diversity of plant body. An exception is the multinucleate and nonseptate *Vaucheria*, a filamentous alga of damp, shady soil, which has highly evolved sexual reproductive structures [Fig. 8-1]. The yellow-green algae will not be discussed further in this book.)

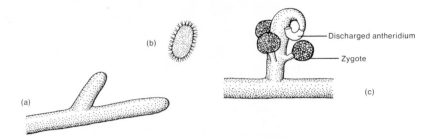

**Figure 8-1.** *Vaucheria*, a yellow-green alga (Xanthophyta). (a) Portion of the nonseptate, multinucleate (coenocytic) thallus. (b) Multiflagellate mitospore (zoospore) with numerous, paired flagella. (c) Sexual reproductive structures consisting of a terminal antheridium and, in the species shown here, four subterminal oogonia (three of the four are visible). In some species, a single oogonium is borne on the main vegetative filament adjacent to the antheridium.

### Golden Algae

Golden algae (Chrysophyceae) are predominantly unicellular organisms, although both colonial and filamentous types are known. Unicellular and colonial golden algae are either nonflagellated or flagellated. Flagellated forms generally possess either a single tinsel flagellum or one tinsel and one whiplash flagellum (Fig. 8-2). A rigid cell wall may or may not be present. Many of the unicellular and colonial forms are coated with calcium carbonate, or *siliceous*, scales on the outer surface of the protoplast. Detailed studies with the electron microscope have shown the origin of the siliceous scales to be within vesicles

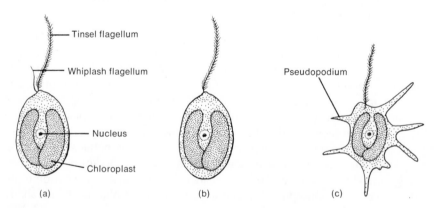

**Figure 8-2.** Golden algae. (a) *Ochromonas*. (b) *Chrysamoeba*, free-swimming form. (c) *Chrysamoeba*, amoeboid form.

pinched off from Golgi bodies in the cytoplasm. The vesicles move through the cytoplasm toward the apical end of the cell, and as they move the siliceous scales grow in size. The mature scale passes out through the cell membrane at a specific location near the flagellar base. Subsequently, the scales move over the surface of the cell exterior. In many cells, there is a complete coating of overlapping scales. The form of the scales is useful in taxonomy. Golgi body function (the packaging of materials for extracellular transport) in these algae is similar to that of other organisms, although the material packaged is different.

Algae that lack a wall may either have a definite cell shape or be amoeboid with radiating cytoplasmic processes called *pseudopodia* (pseudes = false; podion = foot). Moreover, some golden algae have a characteristic shape during certain growth phases and are amoeboid during others. *Chrysamoeba* (Fig. 8-2b) spends much of its life as a flagellated, free-swimming unicell with a definite cell shape. However, it also sends out radiating cytoplasmic processes and becomes amoeboid (Fig. 8-2c). It may even temporarily lose its flagellum. After a period of amoeboid existence, the flagellum reappears and the cell swims away. In both phases, *Chrysamoeba* is photosynthetic. It is of interest that permanent loss of the flagellum in a *Chrysamoeba*-like form would result in the origin of a permanently amoeboid golden alga. Several similar forms exist in nature. Loss of chloroplasts would result in a form similar to those of amoeboid protozoans. Nonphotosynthetic golden algae are also known; these algae resemble pigmented ones in their cellular structure and food reserve.

Reproduction in the golden algae is relatively simple. Asexual reproduction in many of them is by means of flagellated mitospores (zoospores). Sexual reproduction appears to be rare; at least it has been observed only infrequently. Many golden algae survive unfavorable conditions by the formation of endogenous cysts within the cells. The walls of these cysts are often highly ornamented with short spines and consist of two parts: a silicified "bottle" and a nonsilicified "plug." Upon advent of favorable conditions, the plug is dissolved and the alga emerges.

The color of golden algae is due to the carotenoid pigment fucoxanthin, which masks the green chlorophyll. Some species have a second chlorophyll pigment, chlorophyll $c$, in addition to chlorophyll $a$. Fucoxanthin is found in the chloroplasts and, like the chemically unrelated phycobiliproteins of red and blue-green algae, participates in photosynthesis by the transferral of trapped radiant energy to chlorophyll $a$. Even though they are photosynthetic, most if not all golden algae can satisfy their carbon needs by means other than photosynthesis. For example, *Ochromonas* (Fig. 8-2a) is capable of photosynthesizing all the carbon compounds it needs from carbon dioxide, when grown in the light (except for vitamins that must be present in the medium). *Ochromonas* can also obtain carbon compounds from the surrounding medium both by movement of low-molecular-weight substances across the cell membrane and by ingestion of solid food particles (called *phagocytosis*) (phagein = to eat; kytos = a cell; osis = a state or process). Phagocytosis occurs in a specific region of the cell, near the flagellar base. The general process of phagocytosis is diagrammed in Fig. 8–3. By means of phagocytosis, species

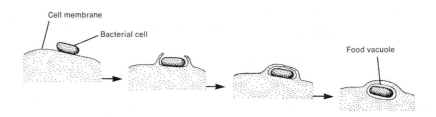

**Figure 8-3.** Diagrammatic sequence illustrating the process of phagocytosis (the ingestion of solid food particles).

of *Ochromonas* can grow in complete darkness. The relative importance of alternative types of nutrition under natural conditions is unknown. Few critical studies have been made on the nutritional requirements and capabilities of golden algae (except for selected Chrysophyceae), because we have not yet been able to culture most of these organisms. Nonetheless, these algae appear to be good research tools in the study of growth, emzyme induction, and the relationship between heterotrophic and autotrophic modes of existence.

### Diatoms

Diatoms (Bacillariophyceae) resemble golden algae in the possession of both chlorophyll *a* and *c* and fucoxanthin. Excess photosynthate is stored as oil droplets in the cytoplasm or as chrysolaminarin.

Diatoms are extremely widespread aquatic and soil organisms, and they are especially abundant in marine waters, where they make a major contribution to the world's carbon dioxide fixation and oxygen evolution. Form of the cell, and number and distribution of striations, punctuations, and other markings on the cell wall are the basis of diatom identification (Figs. 8-4; 8-5). None of the vegetative cells are flagellated. (The only flagellated cells are the sperm of a few marine diatoms; biflagellate sperm have one tinsel and one whiplash flagellum.) Planktonic species commonly possess flattened cells, colonies, or filaments, or have elongate processes that increase the surface area relative to cell volume (Fig. 8-5). Such modifications are assumed to retard the rate of sinking of these planktonic plants. There is also evidence that adjustment in the amount of oil food reserve in the cell regulates the buoyancy of planktonic

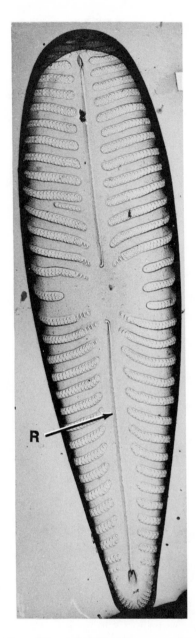

**Figure 8-4.** Carbon replica of the cell of *Gomphonema olivaceum,* showing cell wall markings and raphe. Courtesy of Dr. R. W. Drum, University of California, Los Angeles; from R. W. Drum, *Österr. Bot.* 116:321–330 (1969).

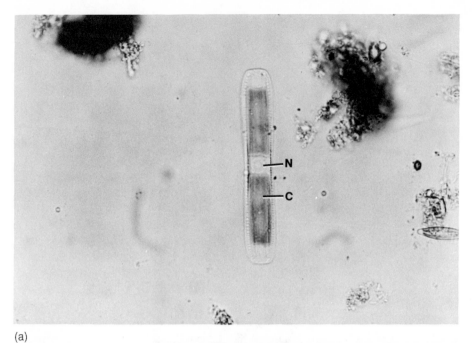

(a)

(b)

**Figure 8-5.** Diatom cells. (a) *Pinnularia,* showing nucleus (N), chloroplasts (C), and cell wall markings. (b) Planktonic diatoms from Lake Michigan, showing flattened and elongate cells.

diatoms. Gas vacuoles, characteristic of the nonflagellated blue-green algae, do not occur in diatoms.

Water blooms of oil-storing diatoms are common at certain times of the year in bodies of water such as Lake Michigan, where the siliceous cell walls may clog water filtration systems. Moreover, if the cells on the filters are disrupted, oils are released and impart a characteristic flavor to the drinking water.

Perhaps the most striking characteristic of diatoms is the presence of silica in the cell wall. Silica (the basic constituent of glass, sand, and granitic rock) is associated with pectic substances, but the spatial and chemical relationship between these two wall components is not yet known. Utilization of silica by diatoms and other chrysophytes offers some interesting problems for study. Silica compounds are relatively insoluble and are normally present in water in very low concentrations. Diatoms absorb these compounds (probably as orthosilicic acid) and deposit them in the wall against a concentration gradient. Deposition of silica in the wall is a continuous process throughout the life of the cell. It occurs in light and dark, in rapidly dividing cells, and in cells in which divisions have been inhibited experimentally. Silica uptake has been shown to be an aerobic process and is blocked by respiratory inhibitors (such as cyanide and fluoride). No other substance has been found to replace silica.

Although there have been a few reports of silica-free cells appearing spontaneously in cultures, there is no evidence that these cells are capable of continued growth and cell division. Silica-free cells are nearly spherical in shape and lack striations and other definitive markings of normal cells. Silica metabolism, transport, and deposition are subjects of active research.

When the cell dies, silica in the wall immediately begins to dissolve. However, where conditions prevent rapid silica dissolution extensive accumulations of silica walls occur. Deposits of fossil marine diatoms over 1,200 feet thick are known. Because the silica walls are very hard and chemically inert, these deposits of fossil diatoms, called *diatomaceous earth,* are mined for industrial use. Diatomaceous earth is used in insulation, as a filtering agent, and as an abrasive.

The presence of two overlapping halves in the cell wall results in a unique type of cell division. After the nucleus divides, the cytoplasm separates into two roughly equal halves. As indicated in Fig. 8-6a–c, the cytoplasm of each daughter cell then deposits a new half of a cell wall. Subsequent enlargement of the daughter cells pushes apart the overlapping halves of the original cell and, in unicellular diatoms, the daughter cells become free. Each daughter cell has half the original cell wall and has synthesized the other half of the two-piece wall. The new wall piece always forms within the old one (Figs. 8-6; 8-7).

One half the progeny of each division is always slightly smaller than the parent cell, and with time there may be a gradual decrease in size of some of the cells of the population. Restoration of maximal cell size is accomplished by sexual reproduction. Diatom cells are diploid, and meiosis precedes sexual reproduction. The zygote, called an *auxospore* (auxo = increase), is formed by the fusion of two haploid protoplasts. The auxospore, with its naked protoplast,

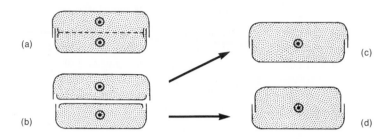

**Figure 8-6.**    Stages in division of a diatom cell.

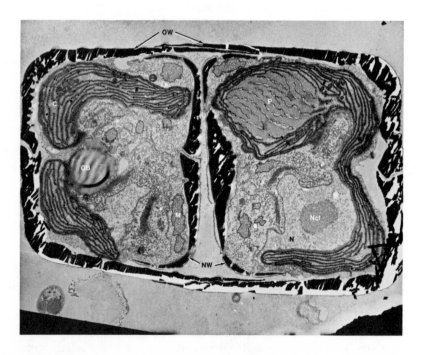

**Figure 8-7.**    Electronmicrograph of a recently divided diatom cell. Note old wall (OW), new wall (NW), nucleus (N), nucleolus (Ncl), chloroplasts (C), pyrenoid (P), mitochondria (M), and oil body (OB). Courtesy of Dr. R. W. Drum, University of California, Los Angeles; from R. W. Drum and H. S. Pankratz, *J. Ultrastructure Research* 10:217–223 (1964).

rapidly increases in size and then secretes a siliceous wall that exhibits the maximum cell size of the species.

The vegetative cells of some diatoms are motile even though they are non-flagellate. These forms have longitudinal striations called *raphes* on both the upper and lower surface of the cell (Fig. 8-4). The raphe is a fissure in the wall, and recent evidence indicates that diatom locomotion is caused by secretion of material through the raphe. All motile diatoms have raphes, but all diatoms that have raphes are not motile, perhaps because these diatoms have lost the ability to secrete mucous through the raphe.

## Summary

| Group | Photosynthetic Pigments | Flagella | Food Reserve |
|---|---|---|---|
| Golden algae | Chlorophyll *a* Chlorophyll *c* Fucoxanthin | Mostly one tinsel, or one tinsel and one whiplash | Chrysolaminarin; oils |
| Diatoms | Chlorophyll *a* Chlorophyll *c* Fucoxanthin | One tinsel and one whiplash | Chrysolaminarin; oils |

*Additional:* eukaryotic cellular structure; basically unicellular or colonial; silica often present in cell wall or in wall of reproductive structure.

### Evolutionary Relationships

The golden algae and the diatoms appear to form a natural group. They have the same photosynthetic pigments and the same food reserves, and their flagellated cells (diatom sperm) may have one tinsel and one whiplash flagellum. Silica deposition is common in both groups. One suggestion is that the diatoms may have evolved from a group of marine golden algae that have silica in their walls.

The similarity in form and position of flagella in Oomycetes (fungi) and golden and yellow-green algae is notable (compare Figs. 3-2d, page 34, and 8-2). The suggestion that the Oomycetes (and possibly some other fungi) evolved from golden or yellow-green algae (for example, a *Vaucheria*-like alga) has been mentioned in Chapter 3. Additional comparative studies are needed.

# 9

---

## Brown Algae

---

Although brown algae, or Phaeophyta (phaeo = brown; phyton = plant), are common plants of rocky seacoasts of all oceans, they have their most luxuriant development along the shores of cold marine waters. Brown algae are attached organisms which, with the exception of *Sargassum,* usually do not survive long when detached from their substrates. *Sargassum* continues growth and undergoes vegetative reproduction by fragmentation when detached, and great quantities accumulate in the large eddy in the Atlantic Ocean known as the Sargasso Sea. Most brown algae grow in the intertidal zone, where they are generally found in places exposed to the full force of wave action. The algae growing in the upper reaches of the intertidal zone are subjected to relatively long periods of desiccation during low tide. The presence of large amounts of moisture-retaining mucilaginous compounds in the cell wall cuts down on the rate of desiccation, however, and normally prevents the algae from drying out completely. Many large brown algae, known as kelp, grow in the lower part of the intertidal zone or in deeper water. The giant kelp, such as *Macrocystis* and *Nereocystis* (Fig. 9-1), often form spectacular underwater forests in deep water.

One of the earliest known uses of brown algae was for fertilizers, and they are still used for this purpose in some areas. At one time, brown algae were the major source of iodine used in "iodized salt," but iodine for this purpose presently comes from other sources. Several kelp, such as *Macrocystis* and

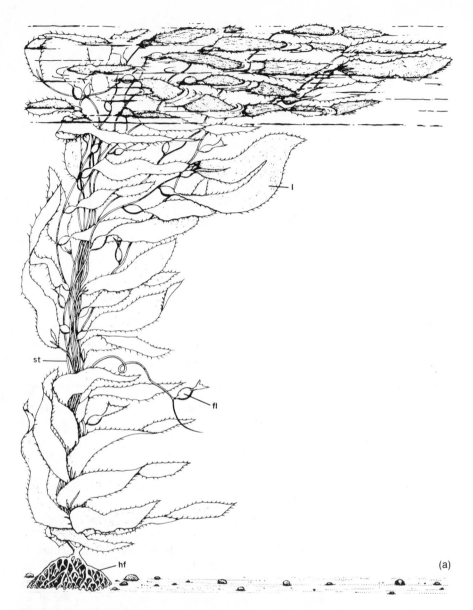

(a)

**Figure 9-1.**    (a) Habit view of *Macrocystis,* showing basal holdfast (hf), and stipes (st) bearing leaf-like lamina (l) with basal floats (fl). (b) Habit view of *Nereocystis,* showing basal holdfast (hf), erect stipe (st), enlarged spherical float (fl), and dense cluster of terminal laminae (l). From Scagel et al., *Plant Diversity: An Evolutionary Approach,* Wadsworth Publishing Co., 1969. Reproduced by permission of the publisher and the authors.

*Laminaria,* now have considerable economic importance because of colloidal compounds called alginates in their cell walls. Alginates have been used as stabilizers in ice cream, sherbet, cream cheese, and whipping cream, and as fillers in candy bars and salad dressing. They have also been used in adhesives, plastics, underwater paint, and waterproof cloth.

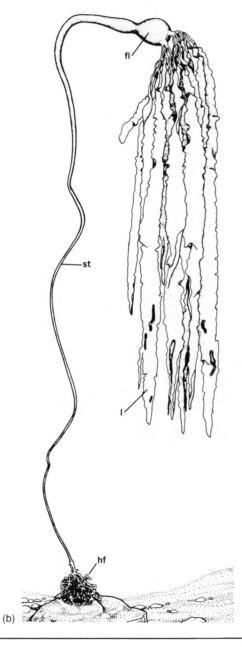

(b)

## General Characteristics

Brown algae have a eukaryotic cellular structure (Fig. 5-7). They possess chlorophyll *a* and *c* and the carotenoid pigment fucoxanthin which gives these plants their brownish coloration. Several chloroplasts (Fig. 9-2) are generally present in each cell, and excess photosynthate usually is stored as *laminarin*, a glucose polymer. The cell cytoplasm is surrounded by a wall of two layers: an inner, rigid, cellulosic layer and an outer, nonrigid, gelatinous layer which may contain the alginates.

Brown algae vary from simple branched filaments with little cell specialization to giant seaweeds over 60 meters long. There are no known unicellular or colonial brown algae. Many brown algae are differentiated into basal holdfast, stemlike stipe, and photosynthetic blade (or frond); these parts functionally resemble the root, stem, and leaf of vascular plants (Fig. 9-1). Three genera of giant kelp (including *Macrocystis* and *Nereocystis*) have specialized cells in the stipe that resemble the food-conducting cells of vascular plants. These

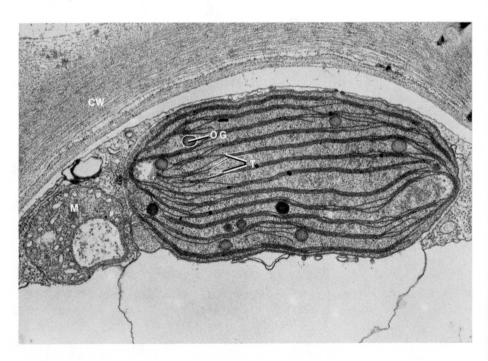

**Figure 9-2.** Electron micrograph of the chloroplast of the brown alga *Egregia*. Stacks of three thylakoids (T) extend nearly the length of the chloroplast and the chloroplast contains several osmiophilic granules (OG). The cell wall (CW) and a mitochondrion (M) are also labeled. Courtesy of Dr. T. Bisalputra, University of British Columbia, Vancouver, from T. Bisalputra and A. A. Bisalputra, *J. Cell Biol.*, 33:511–520 (1967).

cells are presumably involved in the conduction of photosynthate from the blade to the holdfast. Some brown algae, such as *Sargassum,* also possess air floats that keep the photosynthetic parts of the plant near the water surface. Growth in size is commonly initiated by cell division in one or more localized meristematic areas. Three common genera that illustrate the morphological diversity of brown algae are described below.

### Ectocarpus

*Ectocarpus* exemplifies the simplest type of body form in brown algae. It is a small, highly branched, filamentous plant that grows as an epiphyte on other algae. Other than a basal holdfast and reproductive structures, there is little cell specialization.

Its life history is also considered to be simple compared to most brown algae. *Ectocarpus* has what is termed an alternation of isomorphic (isos = equal; morphe = form) generations (Fig. 9-3). In other words, there is a vegeta-

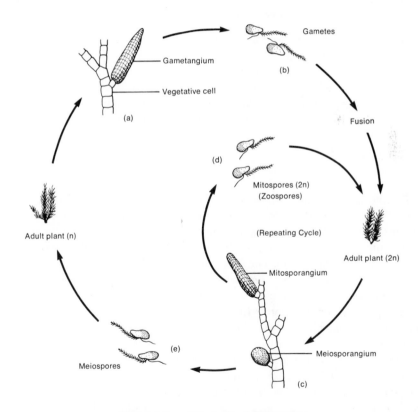

**Figure 9-3.** Life cycle of *Ectocarpus.*

---

**Brown Algae**

tive haploid plant during one stage of development and a vegetative diploid plant during another, and both the haploid and diploid plants are identical in vegetative morphology. The haploid (gametophytic) plant produces multicellular sexual reproductive structures called gametangia. The gametes, which are laterally biflagellated with one tinsel and one whiplash flagella, develop within the gametangia. All the gametes of *Ectocarpus* are alike in size and form and hence are termed *isogametes*.

The diploid (sporophytic) plant results from gamete fusion and zygote germination. There is no prolonged dormancy of the zygote prior to germination. The diploid plant is vegetatively similar to the haploid plant and can be identified only by observation of the reproductive structures and chromosome number. Two types of reproductive structures develop on the diploid plant: mitosporangia and meiosporangia. Mitosporangia are multicellular structures and, in form, closely resemble gametangia of haploid plants. Mitosporangia produce diploid, biflagellate mitospores (zoospores) that germinate and give rise to new diploid plants. Mitospore formation and germination result in a rapid population buildup during favorable growth periods. (The haploid plant has no regular means of asexual reproduction, although unfertilized gametes often develop into new haploid plants.)

The presence of meiosporangia on the diploid plant is the only morphological characteristic by which it is distinguished from the haploid plant. Meiosporangia are unicellular structures (often confused with epiphytic unicellular protozoans) in which meiosis occurs. Haploid biflagellated meiospores (zoospores) develop within each meiosporangium. Upon germination, each meiospore gives rise to a new vegetatively haploid plant that produces gametangia.

**Laminaria**

The life history and differentiation of the plant body of *Laminaria* are characteristic of the group of brown algae known as kelp. *Laminaria* is a common inhabitant of the lower part of the intertidal zone. Similar to *Ectocarpus*, it has an alternation of generations. However, the two generations are dissimilar in form: they are heteromorphic (heteros = other) (Fig. 9-4). The haploid plant is microscopic and filamentous, while the diploid plant is macroscopic and parenchymatous. Because it is large and easily collected, one thinks of the diploid plant when the name *Laminaria* is mentioned. The diploid plant is differentiated into blade, stipe, and holdfast. The blade, which is the primary photosynthetic part of the plant, grows in length by a meristematic zone at the juncture of blade and stipe. At certain times of the year, groups of cells on the surface of the blade enlarge above the blade surface and differentiate into meiosporangia. Haploid meiospores develop within the meiosporangia. The meiospores are released and give rise to haploid plants upon germination.

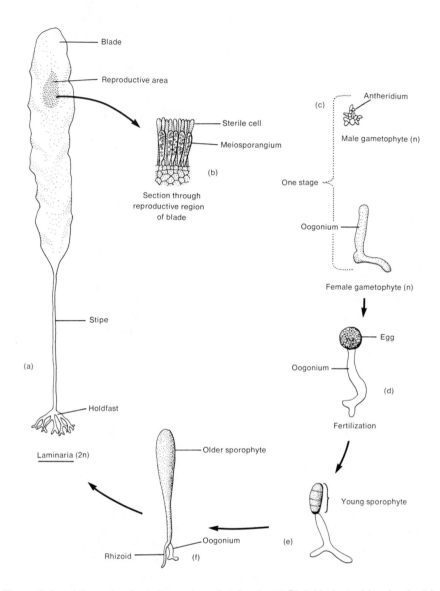

**Figure 9-4.** Life cycle of a kelp, such as *Laminaria*. (a) Diploid plant of *Laminaria*. (b) Section of reproductive area of blade, showing meiosporangia. (c–f) Haploid plants and early development of the diploid plant. (c–e) are drawn to the same scale. (c) to (f) drawn from a slide provided to the author by Dr. J. R. Stein, University of British Columbia, Canada.

There are two kinds of haploid plants: male and female. Both plants are filamentous, but the female plant is less branched and has somewhat larger cells than does the male. During sexual reproduction, a cell of the female plant develops into an oogonium. When mature, the egg is extruded from the oogonium but remains attached to the pore through which it passed. Sperm are produced in antheridia on side branches of the male plant. The biflagellate sperm swim to the nonmotile egg (by an apparent chemotactic attraction), and the fusion of sperm with egg results in the formation of the zygote. As in *Ectocarpus,* the zygote immediately germinates to give rise to a new diploid plant.

In addition to being a source of alginates, *Laminaria* is widely used as food in the Orient, especially in China. Because of its culinary importance, considerable research has been done on the ecology, development, and reproduction of this plant, with the result that *Laminaria* is now cultivated in China much as a crop plant would be. Mature blades with meiosporangia are collected and brought into the laboratory, where the gametophytes and young sporophytes are cultured. When conditions are favorable, the diploid young algae are "planted" in marine bays and allowed to grow to maturity. Seaweed culture has resulted not only in the development of a stable economic crop, but also in the growth of *Laminaria* in areas in which it does not normally occur.

**Fucus**

*Fucus* (Fig. 9-5) is a representative of one of the most advanced brown algal groups, the rockweeds. Fucus and its relatives are usually the dominant organisms of the upper intertidal zone of rocky coasts. Complete desiccation during low tide is prevented by the presence of large amounts of mucilaginous material (termed "*Fucus*-mucus" by an elementary student). As in *Laminaria,* the dominant phase of growth of *Fucus* is the diploid generation. The diploid plant is differentiated into a holdfast and a dichotomously branched axis which often contains air bladders. Growth in length of the plant is initiated by a single cell at the apex of each branch. Increase in diameter of the axis is initiated by the activity of a lateral meristematic zone called a *meristoderm.*

The reproductive structures of *Fucus* develop within small chambers, called *conceptacles,* at the swollen branch tips. Depending on the species, the male and female reproductive structures may be borne on the same plant (hermaphroditic condition), or on separate plants (unisexual condition) (Fig. 9-6). The antheridium develops on a short branch within the conceptacle. The single diploid nucleus of each undergoes meiosis to form four haploid nuclei. Each haploid nucleus then usually undergoes a series of four mitotic divisions, so that a total of 64 sperm are formed within each antheridium. The oogonium develops at the distal end of a two-celled branch within the conceptacle. The diploid nucleus also undergoes meiosis, and each haploid nucleus divides once mitotically, so that a total of eight eggs develop within each oogonium.

Water loss during low tide results in shrinkage of tissues of the parent plant and detachment of the antheridia and oogonia within the conceptacles. Swelling of the mucilaginous material when wetted by the incoming tide results in the extrusion of the sperm and eggs from the conceptacle opening into the water, where fertilization takes place. The small, motile sperm are attracted to the large, nonmotile egg by a chemotactic substance. Germination of the zygote occurs soon after fertilization.

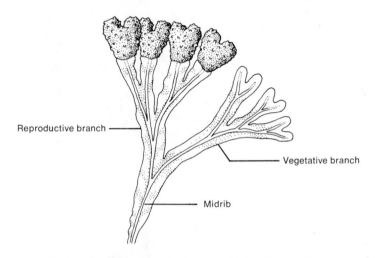

**Figure 9-5.**   Habit sketch of a portion of a plant of *Fucus.*

*Fucus* differs from both *Laminaria* and *Ectocarpus* in that it lacks an alternation of multicellular generations. The vegetative phase is diploid; the haploid phase is represented only by the gametes.

**Summary**

| Photosynthetic Pigments | Flagella | Food Reserve |
|---|---|---|
| Chlorophyll *a* | One tinsel and | Laminarin |
| Chlorophyll *c* | one whiplash | |
| Fucoxanthin | | |

Additional: eukaryotic cellular structure; flagella laterally inserted; largest and vegetatively the most complex of algae; primarily marine intertidal organisms of cold water.

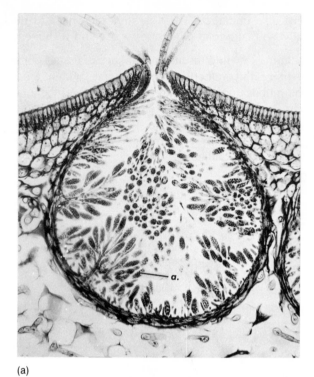

(a)

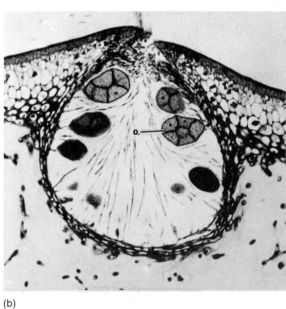

(b)

**Figure 9-6.** Gametangia of *Fucus*. (a) Male conceptacle; antheridium (a), (b) Female conceptacle; oogonium (o).

## Evolutionary Relationships

Brown algae form a well-defined group of multicellular organisms. They resemble the golden algae (Chrysophyta) in a number of respects, including flagellar form, pigmentation, and food reserve. This similarity will be further documented if there is confirmation of the recent report that silica is associated with the cell wall of some brown algae. On the other hand, the manner of flagellar insertion differs: there is lateral insertion in brown algae and approximately apical insertion in golden algae. (The manner of flagellar insertion in brown algae resembles that in the secondary mitospores of Oomycetes, such as *Saprolegnia.*)

It is curious that brown algae lack unicellular forms. This could indicate that brown algae evolved from filamentous ancestors, or that they evolved from now extinct unicellular organisms. A third possibility is that unicellular brown algae still exist but have not yet been recognized. They might exist in the still incompletely known marine phytoplankton. A unicellular brown alga might be expected to have flagellation similar to brown algal mitospores, chlorophyll a and c, fucoxanthin, and store laminarin.

# 10

## Euglenoids

The small, well-defined group of Euglenophyta (eu = good; glene = socket of a joint: reference to the ability of many members of this group to change shape) contains both green and nonpigmented organisms. Euglenoids are predominantly fresh-water organisms, although a few are marine. They are often abundant in places where there is a large quantity of organic nitrogenous compounds, such as polluted streams, wet barnyards, and the margins of ponds. Although of little economic importance, euglenoids are useful research organisms.

### General Characteristics

Euglenoids are highly differentiated unicellular organisms with eukaryotic cellular structure. The cell is bounded on the outside by a cell membrane, which is the typical tripartite unit membrane. Immediately within the cell membrane is a structure called a *pellicle* (pellicula, diminutive of pellis = skin), also called a periplast (peri = all around; plastos = formed). The pellicle is not comparable to a cell wall, since it lies wholly within the cell membrane. Cellulose appears to be absent; the pellicle is mainly proteinaceous. Most euglenoids, including many species of *Euglena* (Fig. 10-1a) and *Astasia*, have a pliable pellicle that enables the cell to change shape. This type of movement

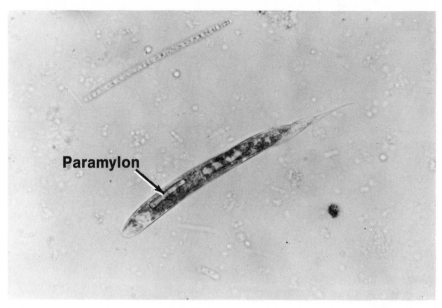

**Paramylon**

(a)

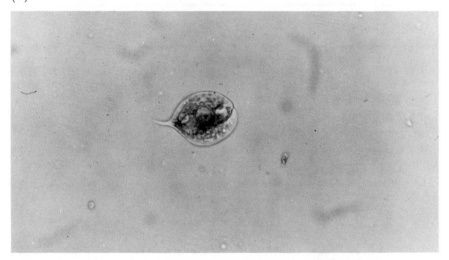

(b)

**Figure 10-1.**   (a) *Euglena* sp. (b) *Phacus* sp.

is called *euglenoid movement*, or *metaboly*. The pellicle of other euglenoids, such as *Phacus* (Fig. 10-1b), is rigid.

The pellicle consists of a series of helically arranged, overlapping strips that extend the length of the cell. A section through a portion of the pellicle is diagrammed in Fig. 10-2. There is a consistent association of microtubules and muciferous bodies with the pellicular strips. The microtubules extend parallel to each strip and are thought to have a skeletal rather than contractile function since they are more abundant in cells with rigid pellicles. It is assumed that secretions by the muciferous bodies provide lubrication to the pellicular strips during euglenoid movement. The cell also contains a large number of Golgi bodies, but their function has not been determined.

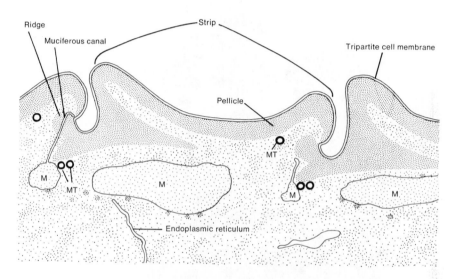

**Figure 10-2.** Diagrammatic representation of the pellicular structure of *Euglena spirogyra*. Note the muciferous bodies (M), the distribution of microtubules (MT), and the muciferous canals passing through the ridge. Reconstruction based on electronmicrographs in G. F. Leedale, *Brit. Phycol. Bull.* 2:291–306 (1964).

The anterior end of the cell is invaginated to form a canal and a reservoir (Fig. 10-5), which in some euglenoids is involved in the ingestion of solid food particles. Osmotic regulation is accomplished by means of one or more contractile vacuoles present near the reservoir. The flagellum of the euglenoids is of the tinsel type but is unique in that a single row of thin, long appendages are inserted along the flagellar axis. Numerous shorter appendages are also present. Euglenoids further differ from other algae in that the eyespot (stigma), appressed to the base of the canal, is independent of a chloroplast (Fig. 10-3). (Eyespots of other algae always form a modified portion of the chloroplast.)

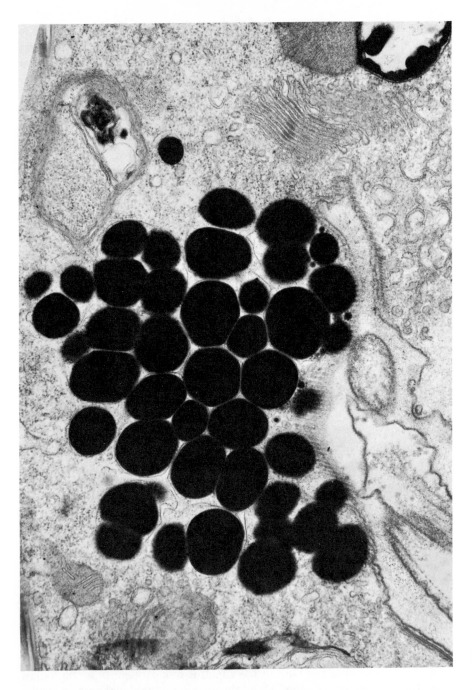

**Figure 10-3.** Portion of the eyespot of *Euglena granulata*. The numerous pigment granules are not associated with a chloroplast. Courtesy of Dr. P. Walne and Dr. H. J. Arnott, Cell Research Institute, University of Texas, Austin.

There exist both photosynthetic and nonphotosynthetic euglenoids. Photosynthetic species contain both chlorophyll *a* and *b*, and their chloroplasts may or may not possess pyrenoids (Fig. 10-4). Excess photosynthate generally is stored as *paramylon* (also called paramylum), a glucose polymer which occurs as granules in the cytoplasm. Most of the euglenoids, including many of the photosynthetic ones, are not completely autotrophic, and require a source of vitamin $B_{12}$. Euglenoids obtain this compound either by diffusion

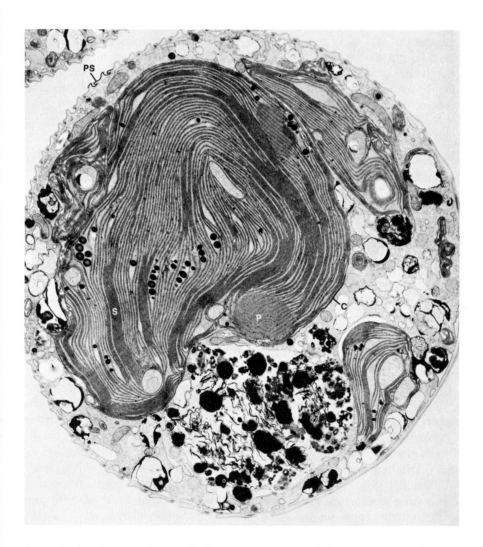

**Figure 10-4.** Electronmicrograph of a cell cross section of *Euglena granulata*, showing a large chloroplast (C) with a pyrenoid (P). Note the stacking of the thylakoids (S) in the chloroplast and the pellicular strips (PS). Courtesy of Dr. H. J. Arnott, Cell Research Institute, University of Texas, Austin.

across the plasma membrane or along with the food ingested as solid food particles. The growth of some euglenoids (especially some species of *Euglena*) is so sensitive to variations in concentration of vitamin $B_{12}$ that they are used as assay organisms to determine the amount of concentration of this vitamin in solution.

Cells multiply through the longitudinal splitting of the unicell into two daughter cells. Chloroplast division soon follows cell division. The behavior of the nucleus is interesting in that the chromosomes remain condensed during interphase, the nuclear envelope does not break down during nuclear division, and the nucleus lacks spindle fibers. This absence of mitotic spindle fibers explains the finding that colchicine does not block mitosis in euglenoids. (Colchicine inhibits mitosis in plants and animals by interfering with spindle fiber formation.) Sexual reproduction has not been confirmed in euglenoids. Cells of this group survive adverse conditions by the formation of dormant cysts. The cells become nonflagellate and secrete a thick mucilaginous coat during encystment.

Members of the genus *Euglena* have been particularly useful experimental organisms, and we have obtained considerable information on cellular structure and function by studying them. This genus and some of the experimental work are described in the following paragraphs.

### Euglena

*Euglena* is a common organism of polluted streams, ponds, and soils of high organic nitrogen content. *Euglena* is not restricted to these habitats, however; different species occur in bogs and other places where there is little available free organic nitrogen.

The cell structure of *Euglena* is shown in Fig. 10-5. It has a nonrigid pellicle, and the cell is capable of creeping movement and of changing its shape. Although a canal and reservoir are present, there is no evidence of the ingestion of solid food particles. (There are statements to the contrary, however, in some textbooks.) *Euglena* has two flagella, only one of which is exerted. The locomotory flagellum is a tinsel flagellum, which arises from a basal granule in the cytoplasm near the bottom of the reservoir and extends out through the canal. The shorter, nonexerted flagellum arises from a separate basal granule, and its tip is attached to the locomotory flagellum within the reservoir. A small swelling, called a *paraflagellar body,* within the locomotory flagellum contains a substance considered to be photosensitive. The paraflagellar body occurs at a point adjacent to the large, red carotenoid-containing eyespot.

One plausible explanation for their proximity is that both the eyespot and the photosensitive substance are involved in the phototactic behavior of *Euglena.* This organism swims through the water in a helical pattern. When swimming toward a light source, *Euglena's* direction of motion is parallel to

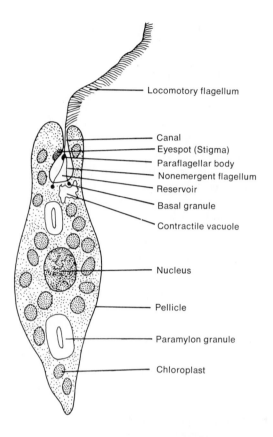

Figure 10-5. Diagram of the cell structure of *Euglena*. The tip of the short, nonemergent flagellum is associated with the locomotory flagellum at about the level of the paraflagellar body.

the light rays, and the paraflagellar body remains unshaded by the eyespot or other cytoplasmic organelles. When the cell swims in a direction other than directly toward a light source, the eyespot periodically darkens the paraflagellar body (because of the helical motion), and this is thought somehow to lead to a continued change in the direction of swimming until the paraflagellar body is again uninterruptedly exposed to light. Although researchers have looked for a specialized cytoplasmic connection between the eyespot and the basal granules of the flagella in electronmicrographs, none has been found. Moreover, there is a report that a *Euglena* without an eyespot still shows phototaxis. These observations lend support to the suggestion that the paraflagellar body on the flagellum is somehow involved in the photoresponses. The mechanism for this response, however, remains unknown.

Although *Euglena* is photosynthetic, possessing several chloroplasts (usually discoidal) with pyrenoids (Fig. 10-4), it can also be cultured in the dark for an extended period of time. When grown in the dark, *Euglena* is unable to utilize exogenously supplied glucose or other hexose sugars as energy sources. On the other hand, dark-grown cultures readily respire organic molecules of shorter chain length such as the two-carbon acetate molecule, and acetate is also assimilated into paramylon. In this ability to utilize only short-chain carbon molecules when grown in the dark, *Euglena* resembles many algae collectively called *acetate algae*. This is a physiological group (containing some green algae, golden algae, and euglenoids) that grows in ecologically similar habitats in nature. Dark-grown cultures lack some of the phosphorylating enzymes necessary for metabolizing glucose, whereas acetate molecules readily enter the respiratory (Kreb's) cycle (see *The Plant Cell*, by William Jensen, this series).

The ability of a few strains of *Euglena* to give rise to cells that are nongreen and thus nonphotosynthetic has been known for many years. Nongreen cells arise when a culture is placed in the dark, or they may arise spontaneously in rapidly growing cultures. In the former case, the cells become green again when placed in light. In the latter case, the nongreen cells are unable to develop chlorophyll; they lack both chloroplasts and proplastids. Whether or not laboratory-derived colorless cells of *Euglena* can survive in nature is unknown. However, a number of naturally occurring nonphotosynthetic euglenoids are known. (In this regard, the colorless saprobe, *Astasia*, which is similar in form to *Euglena*, is of considerable theoretical interest. Because of their morphological and physiological similarity, *Euglena* and *Astasia* are referred to as a "species-pair." [Species-pairs of morphologically and physiologically similar photosynthetic and nonphotosynthetic organisms also occur in golden algae, yellow-green algae, green algae, and blue-green algae.] The above data suggests that *Astasia*-like forms could have evolved from *Euglena* by the loss of chloroplasts, and that they could have evolved more than once. The finding that *Astasia* contains ribulose diphosphate carboxylase, a chloroplast enzyme normally associated with the photosynthetic fixation of carbon dioxide, lends support to this conjecture.)

Two races of a species of Euglena (*Euglena gracilis* var. *bacillaris* and *E. gracilis*, strain Z) have been exceedingly useful in the study of the structure and development of chloroplasts, due to their rapid growth rate (short generation time), ease of culture, and experimental versatility. These two races are very similar to each other, and no attempt will be made to differentiate between them in the following account.

As noted earlier, cells grown in the darkness lose their chloroplasts and become yellowish (due to the continued presence of carotenoid pigments). These cells are referred to as bleached. The bleached cells still contain proplastids, which also divide like chloroplasts, and which enlarge and become green when exposed to light. Light is required for a specific step in chlorophyll synthesis (the transformation of protochlorophyll a to chlorophyll a). This is another example of cells not being able to make use of the genetic information in their nuclei except under the proper environmental conditions. Light is required both for the formation of specific phosphorylating enzymes and for chlorophyll synthesis in euglenoids.

There is a marked increase in new chloroplast proteins and a change in cellular RNA when bleached cells are placed in the light. The chloroplasts contain ribosomes, and study has shown that ribosomes from chloroplasts differ in their base composition and sedimentation rate (in a cesium chloride density gradient) from cytoplasmic ribosomes. In these characteristics, chloroplastidic ribosomes are very similar to ribosomes of prokaryotic (blue-green algal and bacterial) cells. (See the article by L. Margulis, in Suggestions for Further Reading, for pertinent phylogenetic speculations.) Chloroplasts isolated from cells have been found capable of incorporating amino acids into proteins, which indicates that the chloroplast ribosomes can function normally.

Cell bleaching can be induced by a variety of agents besides darkness, including elevated temperatures, ultraviolet (UV) light, and antibiotics such as streptomycin. These agents work in different ways, and each has given additional insight into chloroplast biology.

Streptomycin induces bleaching by interfering with chloroplastidic protein synthesis, but it does not interfere with cytoplasmic protein synthesis. This discrimination appears attributable to differences between the chloroplastidic and cytoplasmic ribosomes mentioned earlier. It is noteworthy that ribosomal protein synthesis in bacteria is also inhibited by streptomycin — another instance of similarity between chloroplasts and blue-green-algal and bacterial cells.

Elevated temperatures (32° to 35° C) differentially reduce chloroplast (and proplastid) division relative to cell division. Each succeeding cell generation has fewer and fewer chloroplasts, so that by the process of dilution colorless cells are finally obtained. Once chloroplasts are lost, they are not regained when the cells are placed in cooler temperatures. This study shows the continuity of chloroplasts from either pre-existing chloroplasts or proplastids for this organism (that is, they do not have de novo origin). The mechanism controlling differential sensitivity to elevated temperatures is undetermined.

Bleaching of Euglena cells by UV light is of interest because of its bearing on the phenomenon of cytoplasmic inheritance. Experiments indicate that UV light apparently causes bleaching by interfering with chloroplast (and proplastid) division, but not with cell division. Existing chloroplasts become diluted out, and bleached cultures, which are unable to re-green, develop. The use of UV microbeams, which can selectively irradiate small portions of a cell, has shown that no bleaching occurs when the nucleus is irradiated. Bleaching occurs only when the cytoplasm (with the nucleus carefully shielded from radiation) is exposed to the microbeam. UV sensitivity occurs only in the chloroplasts, and experiments have shown that the wavelengths most effective in causing bleaching are those most strongly absorbed by DNA. These findings indicate the presence of DNA in the chloroplasts of *Euglena*.

Other experiments have confirmed the presence of DNA in chloroplasts. When the extractable DNA of *Euglena* cells is ultracentrifuged across a cesium chloride density gradient, three distinct bands are found—a main band of nuclear DNA and two smaller satellite ones. On the other hand, UV bleached cells that lack chloroplasts (and proplastids) also lack one of the satellite bands. Conversely, dark-grown cells that have proplastids do contain this satellite DNA band. Thus one of the satellite bands comes from DNA extracted from chloroplasts. The second band of satellite DNA has been shown to derive from the mitochondrial fraction. The existence of distinctive chloroplastidic and mitochondrial DNA has now been demonstrated in a number of plants and animals, and this is probably a universal feature of eukaryotic cells. The function of this DNA is under active research, and the discovery of DNA in chloroplasts and mitochondria has spurred new interest in the study of the function (and phylogeny) of these self-duplicating cell organelles. The apparent lack of sexuality in *Euglena gracilis* and other euglenoids, however, limits its use in studies on cytoplasmic inheritance.

### Summary

| Photosynthetic Pigments | Flagella | Food Reserve |
|---|---|---|
| Chlorophyll *a* | One or more tinsel | Paramylon |
| Chlorophyll *b* | | |

*Additional:* highly differentiated cells with eukaryotic cellular structure; pellicle; pellicular strips; canal; reservoir; interphase chromosomes remain condensed; cysts; sexuality not confirmed.

### Relationships

Euglenoids display a combination of characteristics not found in other organisms. Some biologists contend that euglenoids are related to the green algae, because of the presence of chlorophylls *a* and *b* in both groups. This alone, however, hardly seems justification for assuming a close phylogenetic relationship, since so many other details of cellular organization are different. A distant relationship between euglenoids, yellow-green algae, and dinoflagellates (two groups not discussed in this volume) has also been suggested and needs additional comparative work.

Based on our present information, the classification of euglenoids in a separate division, the Euglenophyta, appears justified. They form a distinct group. The question of whether they are plants or animals is of no real significance; they have some characteristics considered to be plant-like and others that are animal-like. Whether one classifies them as plants or as animals depends upon his prejudices; in any case, they are distinctive organisms.

# 11

## Green Algae

The green algae and the land (or embryo) plants are placed together in the division Chlorophyta (chloro = green; phyton = plant) because they have the following in common: (1) chlorophylls *a* and *b;* (2) true starch (turns blue in the presence of an iodine solution) as food reserve; (3) starch stored within plastids; and (4) one or more whiplash flagella (when flagellated stages are present). Moreover, they have similar cell structure and cell-wall chemistry. The recent identification of floating cell-plate formation (see Jensen, *The Plant Cell*, this series) during cell division in some green algae serves to further close the gap between green algae and land plants. They differ primarily in the general level of organization of the plant body, including the presence of unicellular gametangia in green algae and multicellular ones in land plants.

Thus constituted, the Chlorophyta contains organisms that range in size from microscopic, unicellular *Chlamydomonas* to multicellular trees like the giant redwoods of California. From man's point of view, this is the most important plant division because of the economic importance of gymnosperms and flowering plants. The seed plants (gymnosperms and flowering plants) are excluded from this book. For convenience, the green algae, bryophytes, and ferns and fern allies are treated in separate chapters. A brief description of green algae follows.

**General Characteristics**

Green algae or Chlorophycophytina (phykos = alga; phyton = plant), have a eukaryotic cellular structure. The cell is usually surrounded by a cellulosic wall, but a few flagellated, unicellular species lack a carbohydrate wall. Like embryo plants, green algae are characteristically autotrophic organisms. Most synthesize all the organic compounds they need, including vitamins, from inorganic substrates. Chlorophylls a and b are the photosynthetic pigments, and starch is formed throughout the chloroplast, although the pyrenoid is the primary site of starch deposition. A few green algae lack chlorophyll and hence lead a heterotrophic existence. Heterotrophic green algae are considered to have been derived from autotrophic species by the loss of chlorophyll and associated biosynthetic mechanisms. Achlorophyllous green ·algae form species-pairs with photosynthetic species such as *Chlamydomonas* and the nonphotosynthetic *Polytoma*. Electron microscopy has shown that *Polytoma*, an acetate alga, possesses colorless plastids called leucoplasts. Starch is stored within the leucoplasts. No known green algae, photosynthetic or otherwise, ingest solid food particles (as do some chrysophytes and euglenoids).

Green algae form one of the largest algal groups. A few representative species are shown in Figs. 5-5, page 93, and 11-1. Green algae are found in a wide variety of habitats, including the surface of snow (*Chlamydomonas nivalis*) and tree trunks (*Pleurococcus*). *Pleurococcus* commonly forms green patches on tree trunks and is notable in that its vegetative cells are capable of surviving rapid temperature fluctuations and frequent periods of desiccation. Some green algae are components of lichens, and some live in the bodies of protozoa and *Hydra*. Most green algae are aquatic and are common in fresh and marine waters. Fresh-water species are more abundant and exhibit great morphological diversity, while marine species are often larger.

Green algae from the same kind of environment (marine or fresh-water) appear to have the same kind of life history. Most marine green algae either have a well-defined alternation of generations (isomorphic or heteromorphic) or are vegetatively diploid. In the vegetatively diploid algae (as in the brown alga, *Fucus*) gametes are the only haploid cells present. Very few marine green algae have dormant stages in their development, a condition that may be related to their ecology, since the ocean affords a relatively stable environment for the year-round growth and development of algae.

On the other hand fresh-water green algae, with few exceptions (members of the order *Cladophorales* are exceptions), do not possess an alternation of multicellular generations. In these algae, the haploid, gamete-producing generation (gametophyte) is the vegetative plant. The diploid stage — the result of sexual reproduction — consists of a single cell, the zygote. This zygote soon develops a wall about itself and forms a dormant, resistant structure. Lakes, swamps, ephemeral pools and puddles, high mountain streams, large rivers, snow, soil, and trees are some of the habitats of fresh-water green algae. Most of these algae exhibit seasonal growth periods, determined by the physical factors of the environment. Ephemeral pools soon dry up, and many fresh-water bodies are subjected to wide temperature fluctuations, changes in acidity and alkalinity, and mineral ion depletion. The advent of conditions unfavorable for vegetative growth, such as nutrient depletion, causes changes in cellular metabolism. This is followed by the development of sexual reproductive structures and gametes. In turn, sexual reproduction leads to the development of the dormant stage, or dormant zygote, by means of which most fresh-water algae survive unfavorable growth periods.

Formation of a dormant stage is a noteworthy process because it is not an essential consequence of sexual reproduction itself. It is not a characteristic of sexually reproducing marine green algae. Dormant zygote formation appears to be a specific adaptation to life in the fresh-water environment.

Other species of fresh-water green algae have additional means by which to survive unfavorable conditions. Some produce thick-walled asexual spores. Upon germination, these spores give rise to new haploid plants. Relatively few (for example, *Pleurococcus*) survive adverse periods with unmodified vegetative cells.

Practically all algal body types occur in green algae. Unicellular and colonial forms, either flagellated or nonflagellated, are found. Branched and unbranched filamentous species are common. Some filamentous species have a single nucleus per cell; others are multinucleate. A few green algae — mostly marine plants — are *parenchymatous*, that is, consisting of a tissue composed of living, thin-walled, randomly arranged cells. Others consist of multinucleate tubes with crosswalls forming only in association with reproductive structures. The amoeboid cell is the only body type not found in green algae. (Even forms that lack a carbohydrate cell wall possess a definite cell shape.)

For a thorough representation of the range in morphological diversity of green algae and a pertinent discussion of algae and fungi, the student should refer to G. M. Smith's books *The Fresh-Water Algae of the United States* and *Cryptogamic Botany*, Vol. 1 (see Suggestions for Further Reading). Only a few examples of green algae will be given here.

### Chlamydomonas

*Chlamydomonas*, a motile unicellular organism, is one of the most common green algae in nature and one often studied in elementary biology courses. Present-day representatives are generally considered to have changed little from the first evolved green algae. That is, *Chlamydomonas* is thought to represent a primitive green algal type. A study of this organism should yield insight into the basic cellular form and function of plants in this algal group.

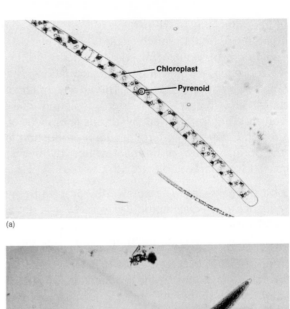

(a)

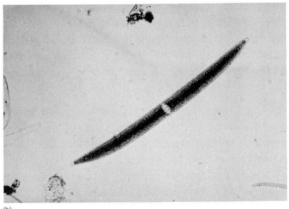

(b)

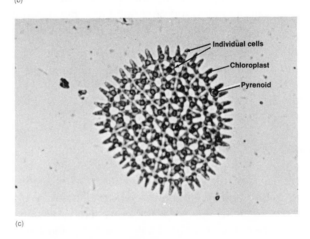

(c)

**Figure 11-1.** Representative green algae. (a) *Spirogyra*. (b) *Closterium*. (c) *Pediastrum*, a colony composed of a flat plate of cells. (d) *Scenedesmus*, showing a large pyrenoid in each cell. (e) *Micrasterias*. (f) A recently divided cell of *Cosmarium*.

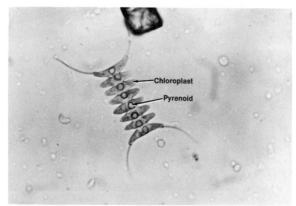

(d)

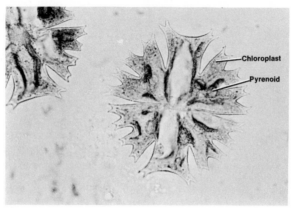

(e)

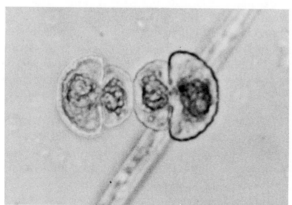

(f)

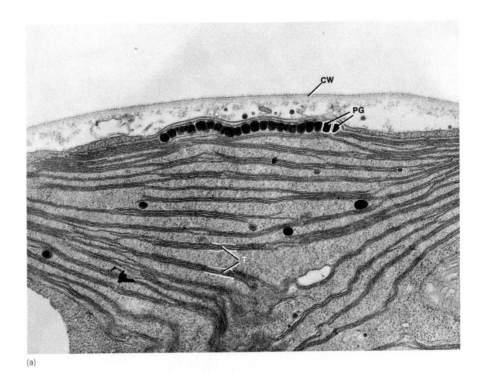
(a)

**Figure 11-2.** (a) Section through an eyespot of *Chlamydomonas*. The eyespot pigment granules (PG) are within the chloroplast envelope. Note also cell wall (CW) and stacks of thylakoids (T) within the chloroplast. Courtesy of Dr. P. Walne and Dr. H. J. Arnott, Cell Research Institute, University of Texas, Austin. (b) Electronmicrograph of a grazing section through the eyespot of *Tetracystis excentrica*, a relative of *Chlamydomonas*. Note the hexagonal packing of the eyespot granules (PG). Courtesy of Dr. H. J. Arnott and Dr. R. M. Brown, Jr., Cell Research Institute, University of Texas, Austin.

(However, it should be kept in mind that no living organisms are primitive. We cannot say that *Chlamydomonas* is a primitive alga. It is possible only to identify organisms that we assume have retained morphological primitiveness. We believe that in many respects *Chlamydomonas* has changed little from ancestral green algal stock.)

*Chlamydomonas* has a relatively simple cellular structure (Fig. 5-6). Motility is provided by two anteriorly inserted whiplash flagella. Two contractile vacuoles occur near the bases of the flagella in the cytoplasm. The large, usually cup-shaped chloroplast is the most conspicuous cellular structure. One or more pyrenoids, associated with starch synthesis, occur in the basal part of the chloroplast. The anterior part of the chloroplast usually possesses

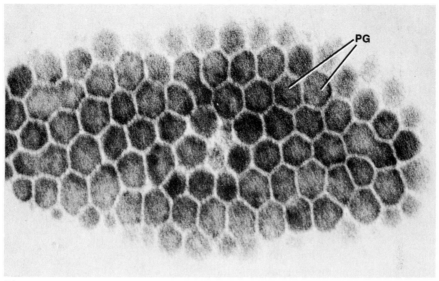

(b)

a reddish-orange carotenoid-containing eyespot. The eyespot, a modified portion of the chloroplast, is composed of one or two layers of tightly packed bodies, hexagonal in section as seen with the electron microscope (Figs. 5-6, page 95; 11-2). The relationship between the eyespot and the phototropic behavior of this organism is not yet well understood. Suspended in cytoplasm in the center of the cell, the nucleus is difficult to observe in the living cell because it is obscured by the surrounding chloroplast. A carbohydrate wall is present exterior to the cell membrane.

Although its structure is apparently simple, Chlamydomonas is functionally complex. This single-celled organism has all the metabolic machinery necessary for photosynthesis, growth, and reproduction. Because of its small size, rapid growth rate, and minimal growth requirements (only carbon dioxide, water, light, and a few inorganic ions are needed), Chlamydomonas is a very useful research organism. Within recent years, it has been used to advantage in physiological, genetic (for studies on both chromosomal and nonchromosomal systems), and biochemical genetic research.

The developmental cycle of Chlamydomonas is quite simple. The young cell enlarges to a certain size, depending on the species, and divides to form new cells. During asexual reproduction, the nucleus usually divides twice mitotically, and the cell divides to form four separate protoplasts within the parent cell (Fig. 11-3a, b). Each cell then secretes a wall about itself and develops flagella. Daughter cells are released into the medium when the parent cell wall ruptures. Formed as a result of mitotic divisions, the flagellated daughter cells are called mitospores (zoospores). Except for its size, each mitospore is identical to the parent cell. Mitospores subsequently enlarge to mature size, at which time asexual reproduction again occurs.

Under appropriate environmental stimuli, cells of *Chlamydomonas* become nonmotile, forming the so-called *palmelloid* stage. Usually the cells in this stage are nonflagellated. Flagella reappear and the cells swim away when favorable conditions return. It is evident that the ability to lose or resorb and to re-form or re-exert flagella, depending on environmental circumstances, is inherent in normally flagellated cells. The capacity to develop flagella is also present in many vegetatively nonflagellated unicellular and multicellular organisms. For example, nonflagellated vegetative cells may give rise to flagellated asexual and sexual reproductive cells.

The process of sexual reproduction in *Chlamydomonas* lends itself well to experimental and observational study. Isogamy, anisogamy, and oogamy have been described in species of *Chlamydomonas,* but practically all research has been done on isogamous species. Most of these studies, in turn, have been made on heterothallic organisms, because the two mating types (plus and minus strains) can be separately cultured. Depletion or inadequate amounts of specific cell metabolites cause the change from vegetative growth to sexual reproduction. Either the vegetative cells themselves are directly transformed into gametes, or gametes are formed by mitotic divisions. There is no morphological difference between gametes and vegetative cells in isogamous species of *Chlamydomonas.* Under suitable conditions, moreover, gametes that do not pair and fuse may divide and give rise to new cell populations. This indicates that there is not a great physiological difference between mitospores and gametes in this organism.

When gametes of opposite mating types are mixed together in a drop of water, they clump into one or more masses. In some species, the clumping response is apparently due to the attraction of the gametes to substances that diffuse from gamete flagella. Flagella also play an important role in the initiation of gamete pairing. Chance flagellar contact of actively motile gametes of opposite mating types, brought into close proximity by the clumping phenomenon, results in the flagella sticking together (Fig. 11-3c). The importance of flagellar sticking in sexual reproduction has been shown by experimental means—ultraviolet-induced mutants of *Chlamydomonas* that lack flagella do not undergo sexual reproduction; they are completely asexual.

In most cases, fusion of gamete cells occurs soon after flagellar cohesion. When cell fusion is complete, the flagella become free, and the zygote often

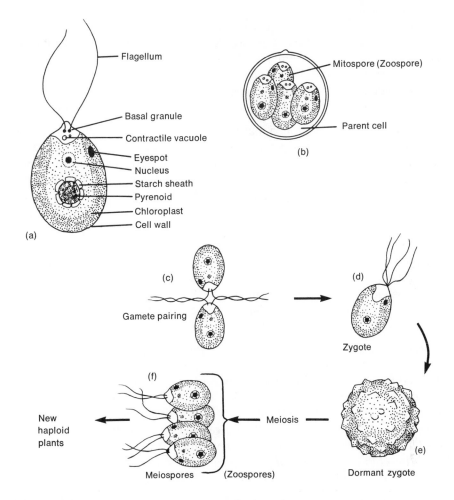

**Figure 11-3.** Stages in the life history of *Chlamydomonas*. (a) Vegetative cell. (b) Mitospore (zoospore) formation. (c–f) Stages in sexual reproduction and resting zygote germination.

swims about as a quadriflagellate cell (see Fig. 11-3d). The period of motility may last for a few minutes or for several weeks, depending on the species and environmental conditions. (Quadriflagellate zygotes of *Chlamydomonas* are similar to, and have been confused with, adult cells of the quadriflagellate green alga *Carteria*.) Ultimately, the zygote loses its flagella, secretes a thick wall, and becomes dormant. Meiosis occurs during the early stages of zygote germination and (usually) four haploid, flagellated meiospores (zoospores) emerge through the ruptured wall.

The process of sexual reproduction in *Chlamydomonas* (Fig. 11-3c–f) is similar to that of isogamous and anisogamous green algae in general. That is, gamete pairing is initiated by flagellar cohesion and followed by gamete fusion. On the other hand, mating in oogamous green algae follows a slightly different sequence, because the nonmotile female gamete (egg) lacks flagella. In this case, the small flagellated male gamete presumably is attracted to the egg by as yet unidentified hormonal compounds. Subsequent steps in sexual reproduction—gamete cell fusion followed by nuclear fusion—are similar.

It was previously mentioned that *Chlamydomonas* is generally believed to resemble a primitive type of green alga. This belief is supported by the relative structural simplicity of *Chlamydomonas* (in comparison with other green algae), its simple developmental cycle, and the fact that adult cells, mitospores, meiospores, and gametes are morphologically similar.

### Ulothrix

*Ulothrix*, a genus of unbranched filamentous organisms, is of considerable theoretical interest. In contrast with *Chlamydomonas*, it shows (1) a differentiation between vegetative cells and gametes (for instance, flagellated reproductive cells develop from nonflagellated vegetative cells); and (2) a simple type of division of labor among cells of the filament.

Most species of *Ulothrix* are fresh-water algae, found in streams, ponds, and lakes. In Lake Michigan, *Ulothrix zonata*, a species with broad cells, grows attached to rocks at or just below the water level, with the result that many of the filaments are exposed to air during low tide. (Lake Michigan is a large enough body of water to be slightly subjected to tidal pull.) Periodic exposure to the air does not harm the cells, however, even though the filaments are exposed to unfiltered sunlight. Like a few other species, *Ulothrix zonata* is a distinctly cold-water plant, appearing in Lake Michigan in the spring, disappearing during the summer, and reappearing in the fall.

The cylindrical cells of *Ulothrix* contain a single nucleus and one parietally arranged, band-shaped chloroplast per cell (Fig. 11-4). From one to several pyrenoids are present, depending on the species. Filaments of *Ulothrix* are attached to the substrate when young, but older filaments may break and become free-floating. Growth in length of the filament is not restricted to a specific meristematic region but, except for the basal cell, occurs throughout the filament. The basal cell, modified into a holdfast, is the only cell in the filament that does not divide or become involved in either sexual or asexual reproduction. Thus *Ulothrix* exhibits a very simple type of division of labor among the component cells of the filament.

The development of flagellated mitospores (zoospores) is the chief means by which a population of *Ulothrix* increases in number. During asexual reproduction, each cell of the filament, except the basal cell, forms one or more quadriflagellated mitospores. When more than one mitospore per cell are formed,

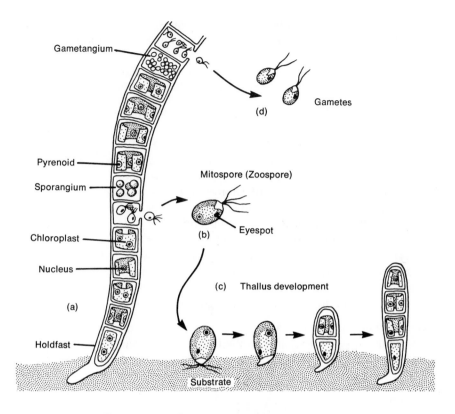

## Chapter 11

Gametangium

Gametes

(d)

Pyrenoid

Mitospore (Zoospore)

Sporangium

Chloroplast

Eyespot

(b)

Nucleus

(c)    Thallus development

(a)

Holdfast

Substrate

**Figure 11-4.**    Stages in development of *Ulothrix.*

the nucleus divides mitotically and the chloroplast and protoplast are divided up (Fig. 11-4a). A pore develops in the lateral wall of the cell in which the mitospores develop, and they are discharged into a gelatinous vesicle. Soon the vesicle wall breaks down, and the mitospores swim away. The mature mitospore has a single, cup-shaped chloroplast, an eyespot, contractile vacuoles, four whiplash flagella, and one nucleus (Fig. 11-4b). *Ulothrix* mitospores, except for being quadriflagellate, resemble *Chlamydomonas* mitospores.

The behavior of *Ulothrix* mitospores is instructive with regard to the possible phylogenetic origin of *Ulothrix*. The mitospores do not have an unlimited period of motility; they ultimately settle down, flagellar end first, on a suitable substratum. Each sessile mitospore then resorbs or loses its flagella and divides repeatedly to form a uniseriate, unbranched filament (Fig. 11-4c). Several points are worth noting here. (1) The anterior end of the mitospore develops into the holdfast cell of the mature filament. (2) The eyespot, as a result of mitotic divisions of the mitospore, ends up in the second or third basal cell of the filament. However, the eyespot, which is not a normal component of the vegetative cell in *Ulothrix*, soon degenerates. (Like the flagella and contractile vacuoles, the eyespot develops *de novo* during mitospore formation.) (3) The filamentous vegetative plant of *Ulothrix* develops from a flagellated cell. This sequence (development of a filamentous plant from a flagellated cell) perhaps indicates one method by which filamentous organisms evolved.

Gametes of *Ulothrix* are formed by mitotic divisions of the nucleus and cleavage of the protoplast. The mature gamete has a single chloroplast, an eyespot, contractile vacuoles, and two flagella (Fig. 11-4d). Except for being smaller and having only two flagella, the gametes are similar in form to mitospores. Gametes of *Ulothrix* resemble *Chlamydomonas* even more than do the mitospores. All species of *Ulothrix* are heterothallic and isogamous. Although they have not been studied with as much precision as in *Chlamydomonas*, the details of gamete pairing and fusion in *Ulothrix* appear to be similar. After gamete fusion, the diploid zygote swims about for a short time and then settles down, secretes a thick carbohydrate wall, and undergoes a rest period. Upon the advent of favorable conditions, meiosis occurs and four haploid quadriflagellate meiospores emerge. Each meiospore then undergoes mitotic divisions to give rise to a new vegetative filament.

Although little experimental work has yet been done on *Ulothrix*, it appears to be a good subject for studies on the factors that initiate asexual and sexual reproduction and the resultant changes in biochemical machinery.

### Enteromorpha

A discussion of *Enteromorpha* (a close relative of *Ulva* [Fig. 5-5f, g], which has the same type of life cycle as *Enteromorpha*) is pertinent, because these organisms indicate how parenchymatous plants might have been derived from filamentous organisms. *Enteromorpha* plants also have a well-defined alternation of multicellular generations not found in previously described green algae.

Most species of *Enteromorpha* are salt-loving, and grow in marine water, inland brine lakes, and salt springs. A few species are found in rivers flowing into the ocean. The mature plant consists of a hollow tube with a wall one cell thick (Fig. 11-5a, b). Its superficial resemblance to an intestine is indicated by the generic name of *Enteromorpha*, literally meaning "gut-shaped." Young plants are attached to the substrate by a single basal rhizoid cell, as in *Ulothrix*, or by several rhizoidal cells. The uninucleate thallus cells each contain a single chloroplast, usually with only one pyrenoid.

During sexual reproduction, gametes may form from any cell of the haploid gametophytic plant except the lower cells. The plants are heterothallic, and gametes are isogamous in most species. Anisogamy has been reported in a few species. Following gamete fusion, the quadriflagellate zygote has a period of motility. Then it settles down, retracts or loses its flagella, and forms a cell wall.

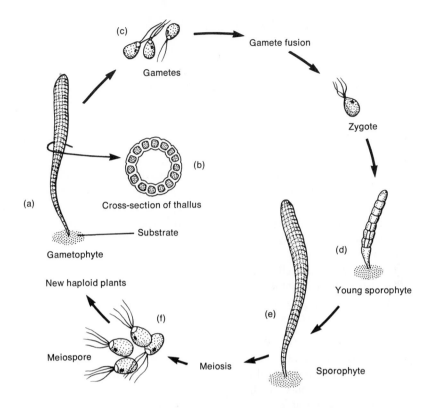

**Figure 11-5.** Stages in the life cycle of *Enteromorpha*.

The first division is mitotic and transverse to the axis of the zygote. The basal cell differentiates into a holdfast, and the upper cell divides repeatedly to form a short filament. Cells of the filament then divide both transversely and vertically, resulting in the development of the parenchymatous adult plant. This is a diploid, sporophytic plant, since it develops from mitotic divisions of the diploid zygote.

The sporophytic plant is morphologically identical with the haploid, gametophytic plant; thus it has an alternation of isomorphic generations. Reproduction in the diploid plant results in the formation of quadriflagellate spores. Cytological study has shown that meiosis precedes development of the flagellated cells; hence they are meiospores. The haploid meiospores are not gametes; they do not fuse. After a short period of motility, they settle down on a substrate, retract their flagella, and undergo mitotic divisions. As in the diploid plant, a short, filamentous, juvenile stage precedes development of the adult parenchymatous plant. The resultant gametophytic plant ultimately forms gametes, as previously described.

During ontogeny of both haploid and diploid plants, *Enteromorpha* passes from a flagellate unicell, to a filamentous plant, to a parenchymatous adult organism (Fig. 11-5). Thus, like *Ulothrix, Enteromorpha* is of theoretical interest. Our discussion of *Ulothrix* ontogeny indicated how filamentous organisms might have evolved from flagellated unicellular ancestors; in *Enteromorpha*, parenchymatous plants might have evolved from filamentous ones.

### Gonium

*Gonium* is a flagellated, fresh-water colonial organism (Fig. 11-6) generally with sixteen cells per colony. Each cell has a typical *Chlamydomonas* structure: two flagella, two contractile vacuoles, a single nucleus, and one cup-shaped chloroplast with a single posterior pyrenoid and an anterior eyespot. The cells are arranged in a flat plate, surrounded by a common gelatinous matrix (readily made visible by the addition of a small drop of India ink to a microscopic preparation). Individual cells are viable when the colony is fragmented, and they give rise to new colonies by asexual reproduction. Cells of *Gonium* are also similar to *Chlamydomonas* cells in that they can pass through a non-flagellated palmelloid stage.

All cells of the colony are capable of asexual and sexual reproduction. During asexual reproduction, each cell of the parent colony divides repeatedly to form a sixteen-celled daughter colony. Upon breakdown of the parent colony, daughter colonies are liberated, the cells being held together by a matrix. Cells of the daughter colonies then enlarge to adult size. No further cell divisions occur.

Gamete formation in *Gonium* resembles daughter-colony formation except that gametes are free from each other when released. Most species are hetero-thallic, and gamete fusion is isogamous. Details of gamete pairing and fusion are similar to those of *Chlamydomonas*. After a period of motility, the quad-riflagellate zygote retracts its flagella and secretes a wall to form a dormant zygote. Germination results in the formation of a four-celled colony. Each of the flagellated cells then gives rise to a new colony by means of asexual re-production. Meiosis occurs during zygote germination.

*Gonium* is the simplest member of a flagellate colonial (*volvocalean*) series that begins with *Gonium* and ends with *Volvox* (Fig. 5-5b, page 93). In this series, there is a progressive increase in cell number per colony (colonies of *Volvox* may have more than a thousand cells), an increase in division of labor between potentially reproductive and wholly vegetative cells, and a change from isogamy to anisogamy and oogamy. In none of the colonial forms do vegetative cell divisions occur; colonies do not increase in cell number after daughter colonies are released from the parent colony. This is unlike the con-dition in *Ulothrix* and *Enteromorpha*, where vegetative cell divisions do occur.

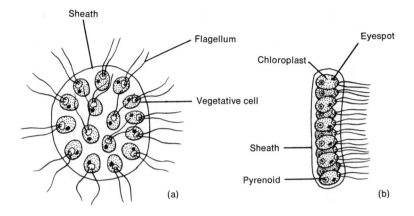

**Figure 11-6.** *Gonium.* (a) Surface view of colony. (b) Side view of colony.

The absence of vegetative cell divisions provides one reason for considering the so-called volvocalean line of evolution to be a dead end, leading neither to the development of higher plants nor animals.

### Acetabularia

Some of the most elegant studies on the nuclear control of form development and the influence of the cytoplasm on nuclear behavior have been carried out on *Acetabularia*. These are marine organisms and can be cultured in the laboratory. The mature plant is a large, single cell, four to six centimeters in length, which is differentiated into basal rhizoids, a chloroplast-containing stalk, and an apical cap. There is a single nucleus, located in one of the rhizoids. Briefly, the general pattern of development is as follows. When the cap is mature, the large basal nucleus divides, and numerous small daughter nuclei move in the cytoplasm throughout the plant. Resting cysts are then formed in the cap, each cyst containing several nuclei. The cysts can be induced to germinate after a period of maturation. During germination, the nuclei in the cysts divide, the cytoplasm cleaves, and biflagellate gametes develop. (Presumably, meiosis occurs during cyst formation.) The gametes fuse when released from the ruptured cyst, and the zygotes develop into new plants. This developmental cycle, which naturally takes about three years, occurs in about one year in the laboratory.

It was early found that when the cap is removed from a plant, a new cap is regenerated. *Acetabularia* is capable of regenerating missing parts, and the nucleus need not be present for regeneration to occur. A new cap forms at the apex of the stalk when both cap and nucleus-containing rhizoid are removed. (New rhizoids seldom regenerate.) Thus regeneration appears to be under immediate control of cytoplasmic morphogenetic substances.

---

**Green Algae**

The next question is whether the appearance of morphogenetic substances in the cytoplasm is under nuclear control or whether such substances are self-duplicating cytoplasmic entities. If self-duplicating entities are present, then new caps should repeatedly form on enucleated stalks following cap removal. It has been conclusively shown that when the first regenerated cap is removed from an enucleated stalk, no further caps develop. In contrast, caps form repeatedly in decapitated nucleated plants. The morphogenetic substances in the cytoplasm of enucleated plants are apparently used up during regeneration of the first cap. Thus the morphogenetic substances are *not* self-duplicating cytoplasmic entities.

Evidence that the origin of the morphogenetic substances is from the nucleus comes from the following kinds of experiments. The stalk of *Acetabularia mediterranea (med)* is cut off just above the rhizoids. To this *med* stump is grafted a stalk (minus the cap) of *Acetabularia crenulata (cren)* (Fig. 11-7). This graft results in a plant with a *med* nucleus and a *cren* cytoplasm. What type of a cap develops? The first formed cap is somewhat intermediate between *med* and *cren* in form. However, removal of this (and later formed caps) is always followed by the regeneration of a cap with *med* form. In the reciprocal graft, an intermediate cap is formed first, followed by the formation of *cren* caps during subsequent regenerations. These results have been interpreted to indicate that the morphogenetic substances already present in the cytoplasm at

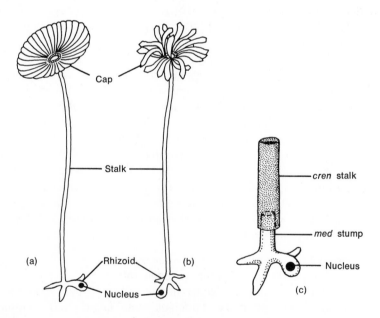

**Figure 11-7.** *Acetabularia.* (a) *A. mediterranea.* (b) *A. crenulata.* (c) A piece of *A.crenulata* stalk has been grafted to the base, with nucleus, of *A. mediterranea.*

the time of grafting are used up during the formation of the first cap and that later formed caps are under complete control of substances arising from the nucleus. It appears, then, that the nucleus exerts its control by the synthesis of substances (messenger RNA?) that are stored in the cytoplasm and play a specific role in directing cap construction.

Not only does the nucleus affect the cytoplasm, but the cytoplasm influences nuclear behavior. It was previously mentioned that when the plant is mature, the nucleus divides to form numerous small nuclei. But what happens when the nucleus of a mature plant, just prior to nuclear division, is transplanted into an immature plant? Does the nucleus go ahead and divide? Experimental results are that the nucleus does not divide and will not divide until the cap of the plant is mature. In a reciprocal experiment, a nucleus from a young plant was transplanted into a mature plant. Here the nucleus began to divide in about two weeks, in contrast to the two months or so that it would normally take. It has been concluded, then, that the state of the cytoplasm influences development of the nucleus.

In summary, the following interpretations of the experimental results may be made: (1) cap formation depends on morphogenetic substances in the cytoplasm; (2) the morphogenetic substances are under nuclear control; and (3) the state of the cytoplasm influences nuclear behavior.

*Acetabularia* has also proved a useful experimental organism for biochemical studies. For example, an enucleated, light-grown plant will continue growth and development for about two months. It can go through complete development up to the point of nuclear division. (Dark-grown enucleated plants quickly die.) The long-term growth of light-grown plants has made possible extensive and continuing comparative studies on the physiology and biochemistry of nucleated and enucleated plants. (Discussion of these investigations, however, is beyond the scope of this book.)

### Spirogyra

*Spirogyra* is a common, filamentous, fresh-water alga. It is often a conspicuous member of algal water blooms. Because of a gelatinous outer wall layer, *Spirogyra* is silky to the touch.

The most striking cellular feature (in fact, the one upon which the genus is based) is the presence of one or more large helical chloroplasts in each cell (Figs. 11-1a; 11-8a). Each chloroplast contains numerous pyrenoids involved in starch synthesis. The bulk of the cell volume is taken up by a large central aqueous vacuole. In the center of the cell, a rather conspicuous nucleus is suspended by radiating cytoplasmic strands. Most of the cytoplasm is restricted to a thin layer surrounding the aqueous vacuole.

A definitive characteristic of *Spirogyra*, and of its relatives such as the des-

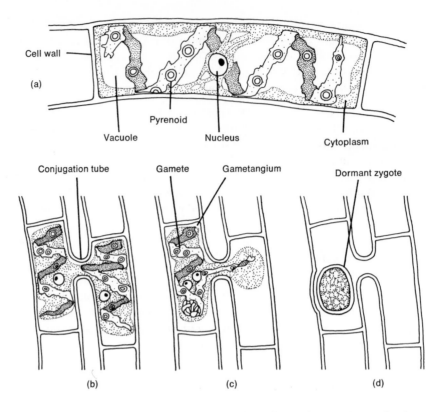

Cell wall

(a)

Pyrenoid

Vacuole

Nucleus

Cytoplasm

Conjugation tube

Gamete

Gametangium

Dormant zygote

(b)

(c)

(d)

**Figure 11-8.** *Spirogyra.* (a) Vegetative cell. (b–d) Stages in sexual reproduction.

mids, is the complete absence of flagellated cells. In *Spirogyra* the filament grows in length as a result of mitotic divisions and cell enlargement. Asexual reproduction occurs by fragmentation of the filament. Sexual reproduction is either homothallic or heterothallic, depending on the species. Gametic union in heterothallic forms is similar but not identical to that already described for the zygomycetous fungus *Rhizopus*. In species of *Spirogyra* under discussion, the lateral cell walls of nearby filaments which are of opposite mating types bulge out slightly toward each other and then grow together. The portion of the wall in contact is dissolved to form a conjugation tube through which one of the gametes passes. Gametes of both mating types are uninucleate, nonflagellated, and similar in form (isogametes). The gamete that moves is often called a "male"; the stationary gamete is the "female." Fusion of gamete protoplasts and nuclei occurs in the cell (gametangium) of the female gamete. This process of fertilization is referred to as *conjugation*. The zygote immediately develops a thick wall and passes into the dormant zygote stage (Fig. 11-8b–d). As in *Chlamydomonas*, meiosis occurs during germination, but in *Spirogyra* only a single haploid cell grows out. Three of the meiotically produced haploid nuclei degenerate prior to wall rupture, so that only one haploid nucleus is functional.

Similar to *Chlamydomonas*, *Spirogyra* has a haploid vegetative growth phase and a diploid, single-celled, dormant stage. The general life history patterns of these two organisms are alike. Only details are different. For example, the coming together of nonflagellated gametes of *Spirogyra* is provided for by the development of a conjugation tube. There is evidence, however, that *Spirogyra* evolved from an ancestor that had flagellated male gametes. This is indicated by the presence of contractile vacuoles in the "male" gamete during its movement towards the "female" gametangium. The "female" (or stationary) gamete lacks contractile vacuoles.

# 12

## Bryophytes

The land plants (sub-division Embryophytina) have many characteristics which are apparently adaptations to terrestrial life. At one time, the bryophytes were separated from the other land plants because of the absence of a lignified water-conducting tissue. However, the importance of this distinction has diminished in recent years, as will be discussed below. It is now recognized that the bryophytes (especially the mosses) have all the distinctive attributes of other land plants.

The land plants have an alternation of heteromorphic generations. In bryophytes, the gametophytic generation is long-lived and the sporophytic generation relatively short-lived. This relationship is reversed in the other land plants. Significantly, the sporophyte of land plants shows more complete adaptation to life on land than does the haploid generation, in many respects.

If not controlled, excess water loss by land plants — no danger for aquatic organisms — may result in their death. The presence of a waxy layer, called a *cuticle*, on the outer surface of the plant apparently is an adaptation for de-creasing the rate of water loss by land plants. The cuticle is characteristic of the sporophyte; it is uncommon on gametophytes except in mosses.

The cuticle not only serves as a barrier against water loss. It also decreases the rate of gas exchange between the photosynthetic tissue of the plant and the atmosphere. This exchange is effected by pores, called *stomata*, in plant tissue, through which carbon dioxide, oxygen, and water vapor diffuse. Stomata, like the cuticle, are attributes of the sporophyte.

The development of a water-conducting system was an important adaptation to terrestrial life, because it meant that not all tissues had to be in contact with water. Plants could grow up into air; only one part, the base, had to be in an aqueous environment. In theory, the more efficient the water-conducting system, the larger the plant. A food-conducting tissue, which carries photosynthate to the base of the plant, generally is spatially associated with the water-conducting system.

Plants that have a water-conducting tissue with lignified cell walls are referred to as *vascular plants;* their water-conducting tissue is called *xylem,* and food-conducting tissue is *phloem.* Xylem and phloem occur in the sporophytic generation; very few gametophytes have xylem. Some bryophytes, especially mosses, also have water- and food-conducting systems. The non-lignified cells of the water-conducting tissue are called *hydroids,* and the food-conducting cells are *leptoids.* There are many points of similarity in form and function between cells of the water- and food-conducting tissues of bryophytes and vascular plants. Callose, a type of carbohydrate that is characteristic of food-conducting cells of vascular plants, has recently been identified in moss leptoids, and lignin has also recently been isolated from gametophytic stems of large mosses (*Dawsonia* and *Dendroligotrichum*). The cellular localization of lignin in these mosses is certain to be studied in the near future. Moreover, other bryophytes (including the liverwort *Marchantia*) that normally do not synthesize lignin can form lignin from eugenol (a lignin precursor). At least some of the enzymes necessary for lignin formation are present in these bryophytes, and lignification should no longer be used as a major criterion to separate bryophytes from the other land plants.

Another attribute of land plants is the occurrence of multicellular gametangia. Both the male gametangium (*antheridium*) and the female gametangium (*archegonium*) have a sterile jacket of cells. The sterile jacket of cells apparently prevents developing gametes from drying out. Sexual fusion in embryophytes is oogamous and occurs within specialized tissue of the female reproductive structure. Subsequent zygote germination and embryonic development of the sporophyte also occur within the protective confines of the female reproductive structure. (Retention of the embryo within maternal tissue is a definitive attribute of land plants.) A discussion of bryophytes follows.

### General Characteristics

Bryophytes, or Bryophyta (bryon = moss), are abundant in, but not restricted to, moist places. Although they grow in both arctic and arid regions, they have their most luxuriant development in tropical climates. They are common soil organisms, and they are *epiphytes* (organisms that live upon other living plants). Bryophytes also grow on fallen logs and unweathered rocks, at entrances to caves, and on roofs and sides of buildings. While bryophytes are land plants, a few are secondarily aquatic in fresh water, but none live in the sea.

Individual species of bryophytes differ considerably in the range of conditions under which they can grow. Species of wide distribution usually grow in a wide variety of habitats. Other species are restricted to specific and often unusual habitats. Plants restricted to specific ecological niches often make good indicator species. For example, bryophytes in Canadian forests have been used as indicators of humidity and soil quality. One group of bryophytes, known as copper mosses, characteristically occurs only on heavy metal deposits such as copper and antimony. Some occur only on dung. Most bryophytes of restricted distribution in nature can be cultured on simple inorganic media in the laboratory. Thus bryophytes of odd habitats do not necessarily have fastidious nutritional requirements; unlike other plants, they can tolerate these conditions.

Bryophytes have little direct economic importance to man, with the exception of *Sphagnum,* a moss that grows in bogs. In such bogs, a combination of acidic conditions and low oxygen availability decreases the rate of bacterial and fungal decomposition of organic matter, making possible the accumulation of extensive deposits of *Sphagnum.* These compacted and partially decomposed deposits are known as *peat;* hence the name of peat moss for this bryophyte. Peat moss is mined and used as fuel in some countries, although *Sphagnum* is not used as widely now as formerly. Because of its tremendous water-absorbent qualities, *Sphagnum* is also used as a soil conditioner. During World War I, some wound dressings were made of *Sphagnum.*

Other bryophytes are of some indirect economic importance to man. Many are "pioneer" organisms—they are among the first plants to colonize rocks, tree trunks, and disturbed soil. These bryophytes modify their environment so that other organisms are able to grow. Pioneer plants are gradually replaced by other plants. Soil bryophytes, especially where they form large mats or grow on otherwise bare soil, aid in soil stabilization and decrease water runoff after rain.

There are three groups of bryophytes: hornworts, liverworts, and mosses. They all possess an alternation of generations in which a multicellular, long-lived gametophytic generation alternates with a multicellular, short-lived sporophytic generation, with the sporophytic plant remaining permanently attached to the gametophyte. One of the few important things that organisms in these groups have in common is the same general type of life history. The relationship of these groups to one another is not yet clear.

Perhaps the manner of sporophyte growth is the best single attribute by which to separate hornworts, liverworts, and mosses. The hornwort sporophyte is an erect structure, differentiated into a capsule region and a basal foot, embedded within the gametophytic plant, with a zone of actively dividing cells—the *intercalary meristem*—occurring in the region between foot and capsule (Fig. 12-1a). As a result of meristematic activity, the capsule increases continually in length; potentially the sporophyte is capable of unlimited growth. In nature, however, this potentiality is never realized.

The liverwort sporophyte, differentiated into capsule, seta, and foot (Fig. 12-1b), does not have a localized region of meristematic activity. Cell divisions occur throughout the developing sporophyte. Then cell divisions cease, and sporophyte maturation occurs. Sporophytic growth is decidedly limited in extent.

The mature moss sporophyte, also differentiated into capsule, seta, and foot, exhibits apical growth during its development. During sporophyte growth the basal end of the young sporophyte penetrates into gametophytic tissue. Cell divisions and cell enlargement at the other end result in growth of the sporophyte into the air. The young sporophyte is spindle-shaped (Fig. 12-1c). Theoretically, the moss sporophyte should be capable of indeterminate growth, but such growth never occurs.

The form of the bryophyte gametophyte is variable. The hornwort gametophyte (Fig. 12-2) is a dorsiventral, thalloid plant anchored to the substrate by means of colorless, unicellular *rhizoids* (rhizoid = root-like). Stomata-like pores, which lead into mucilage-filled chambers, are found on the ventral

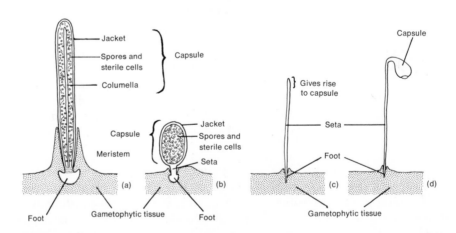

**Figure 12-1.** Form and growth characteristics of bryophyte sporophytes. (a) Hornwort sporophyte, with intercalary meristem. (b) Liverwort sporophyte, with no localized meristem. (c) Young moss sporophyte, with apical growth at each end. (d) Mature moss sporophyte.

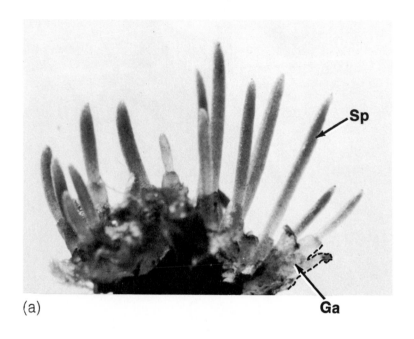

(a)

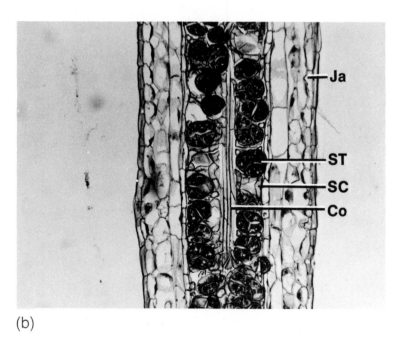

(b)

**Figure 12-2.** Hornworts. (a) *Phaeoceros laevis*, showing both sporophyte (Sp) and gametophyte (Ga). (b) *Anthoceros*, longisection of sporophyte capsule showing jacket (Ja), spore tetrad (ST), sterile cell (SC), and columella (Co).

(a)

(b)

**Figure 12-3.** Liverworts. (a) *Riccia.* Rosette of plants on soil. The gametangia and sporophyte are embedded in the midrib (M). (b) Male and female plants of *Marchantia polymorpha.* Antheridia are embedded in the upper surface of the antheridiophore (An) head; archegonia and sporophytes are pendant from the lower side of the archegoniophore (Ar) head. (c) Gametophyte (Ga) and sporophyte (Sp) of *Pellia.*

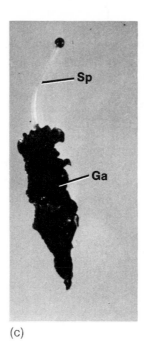

(c)

surface of the thallus in many species. Colonies of blue-green algae (occasionally nitrogen fixers) are often present in these chambers. Each cell of the thallus generally has a single chloroplast with a pyrenoid. This is the only group of embryophytes in which pyrenoids occur, and their presence is considered to be of phylogenetic significance. The gametophyte of most hornworts has no special means to survive conditions unfavorable for vegetative growth. However, a few species form *tubers* (parenchymatous structures full of reserve food).

Gametophytes of liverworts may be either thalloid or leafy (Figs. 12-3; 12-4). The terms *leaf* and *stem* are here used in a functional sense. That is, the stem is the main axis of the plant and it bears or supports lateral photosynthetic appendages, or leaves. It should be noted, however, that stems and leaves of bryophytes are not strictly comparable to those of vascular plants. In bryophytes, they belong to the gametophytic (haploid) generation, while they are sporophytic (diploid) structures in vascular plants.

As in hornworts, the liverwort gametophyte is attached to the substrate by means of unicellular rhizoids. Cells of the plant possess several discoidal chloroplasts without pyrenoids. A few species form tubers. The nature and biosynthesis of tuber food reserve and the factors that control tuber initiation need definitive study in liverworts and hornworts.

Thalloid liverworts are usually soil organisms. The dorsiventral thallus exhibits a characteristic (dichotomous) branching pattern. Plants such as *Marchantia* may exhibit considerable internal differentiation (Fig. 12-5). Note the air pores (functional counterparts of stomata), air chambers, photosynthetic filaments, food-storage tissue (the cells of which lack chloroplasts), scales, and rhizoids. *Marchantia* has a specialized means of vegetative reproduction through the formation of multicellular bodies called *gemmae* within gemma cups. Gemmae are dispersed by wind and water, and upon germination give rise to new gametophytic plants.

There are many more species of leafy liverworts than of thalloid forms. Leafy plants are common soil and epiphytic organisms. A few have radial symmetry and may be quite moss-like in appearance. Most, however, are dorsiventral, the stem bearing two rows of lateral leaves (Fig. 12-4). An additional row of leaves, called underleaves, may or may not be present.

Mosses are the most commonly encountered bryophytes. The adult gametophytes are leafy and generally have radial symmetry (Fig. 12-6). The leafy stems are attached to the substrate by multicellular rhizoids, unlike hornwort and liverwort gametophytes which have unicellular rhizoids. Cells of mosses possess several usually discoidal chloroplasts without pyrenoids. The general pattern of development of moss gametophytes and sporophytes is explored more fully below.

### Mosses

Mosses are common plants of woods, fields, and shaded stream banks, where they often form extensive mats or carpets. They may be found in gardens and lawns, along paths and sidewalks, and on damp, shady sides of brick or cement edifices. Superficially they appear to form a homogeneous group, but close study shows that mosses have considerable morphological (Fig. 12-7) and physiological variation. (The experimental potentialities of this group, and of bryophytes in general, have been largely unexploited.)

It is easiest to begin a discussion of moss development with the spores. Moss spores are unicellular, haploid structures, and often have two important functions. The spores of most mosses are small and light enough to be wind-disseminated. Thus spores may establish plants in new areas. In addition, spores of many mosses are resting structures, remaining dormant without loss of viability for variable periods of time, depending on the species. Specific factors involved in the initiation of spore germination in mosses and other bryophytes have not yet been fully elucidated. It has long been known that spores of many mosses will not germinate in the dark even though other conditions necessary for germination have been met. Light quality, minimum duration of light necessary to induce germination, and pigment system involved in the light response are areas in which further study is needed.

---

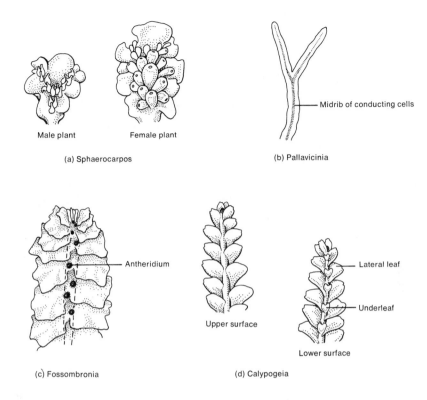

## Chapter 12

Male plant          Female plant

(a) Sphaerocarpos

(b) Pallavicinia

— Midrib of conducting cells

— Antheridium

Upper surface

— Lateral leaf

— Underleaf

Lower surface

(c) Fossombronia                    (d) Calypogeia

**Figure 12-4.**  Liverwort gametophytes.

Spore germination results in the development of the gametophyte. Moss gametophytes have two distinct growth phases: filamentous and parenchymatous. The filamentous or *protonemal* (protos = first; nema = a thread) phase of gametophytic growth develops directly from the germinated spore. Protonema are differentiated into prostrate axial filaments with oblique cell walls and spindle-shaped chloroplasts, from which arise both rhizoidal filaments that penetrate the substrate and erect photosynthetic filaments with discoidal chloroplasts (Fig. 12-8a). This pattern of protonemal growth, called *heterotrichous* (heteros = other; trichos = hair) growth, resembles that of certain green algae. However, cells of mosses possess many chloroplasts, and their chloroplasts lack pyrenoids.

After a period of protonemal growth, the parenchymatous phase of gametophytic growth is initiated. Parenchymatous plants, called *gametophores,* arise from specialized cells that are one cell removed from a prostrate axial filament. This specialized initial cell then divides in different planes to give rise to an apical cell with three cutting faces. Mitotic activity of this apical cell, followed by cell enlargement, results in subsequent gametophore growth. The extent of protonemal growth prior to gametophore initiation is variable, depending on

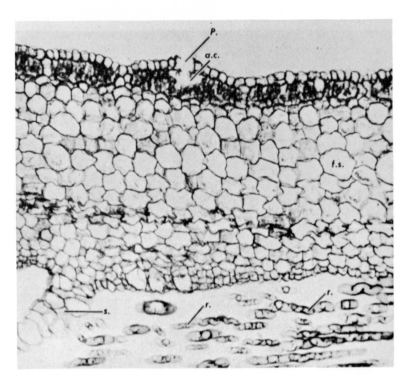

**Figure 12-5.** *Marchantia.* Section of gametophyte showing internal differentiation. Note pore (p), air chamber (a.c.) of photosynthetic zone, nonphotosynthetic food storage zone (f.s.), rhizoids (r), and scale (s).

the species. In some mosses, the protonemal mat may be a few inches in diameter; in others, it may be practically nonexistent.

Gametophore initiation is a noteworthy morphogenetic phenomenon (Fig. 12-8b). First, only certain protonemal cells initiate gametophores (providing an excellent example of genetically identical cells exhibiting divergent potentialities). Second, the timing of gametophore initiation can be altered experimentally, although gametophores of many mosses are normally initiated only after the protonemal mat has reached a certain minimum surface area. For example, light exerts a considerable morphogenetic effect. Protonema cultured under very weak light intensities develop buds only when sugar (such as sucrose) is added to the medium. However, bud initiation does not occur in dark-grown cultures, even when the medium is supplemented with sucrose. It appears that in addition to providing photosynthate, light has a specific formative effect. Experiments on light quality have shown that bud initiation occurs only in cultures illuminated with red light, even though normal protonemal differentiation into axial and photosynthetic filaments occurs in both red and blue light. Thus a red-absorbing pigment is involved in gametophore

**Figure 12-6.** Gametophyte of *Polytrichum juniperinum* grown in agar culture. Note radial symmetry and differentiation into leaf, stem and rhizoids. Courtesy of Dr. H. J. Arnott, Cell Research Institute, University of Texas, Austin.

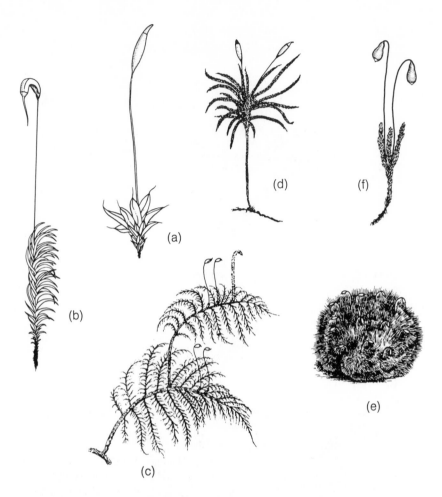

**Figure 12-7.** Diversity in moss gametophytes and sporophytes. (a) *Tortula muralis.* (b) *Dicranum scoparium.* (c) *Hylocomium splendens.* (d) *Climacium dendroides.* (e) *Grimmia pulvinata.* (f) *Bryum* sp. From Scagel et al., *Plant Diversity: An Evolutionary Approach,* Wadsworth Publishing Co., 1969. Reproduced by permission of the publisher and the authors.

initiation under these conditions. However, Polish researchers found in 1963 that the red light requirement could be replaced by the addition of kinetin (a compound that stimulates nuclear division and cell enlargement) to the culture medium. Gametophores were initiated when a moss (*Ceratodon purpureus*) was cultured in the dark in a sucrose and kinetin-supplemented medium. It is expected that much more will be known in the next few years about control and changes in the biochemical pathways during gametophore initiation and development. Another item of interest is that more than one gametophore normally develops from protonema derived from a single spore. Moreover, in most species, gametophore initiation does not inhibit further protonemal growth. Not only may a single protonemal mat give rise to a large number of gametophores, but it may do so over a long period of time. This results in the formation of moss mats.

Gametophores are the mature, long-lived plants of the gametophytic phase of growth. They are the plants we identify as moss. Although part of the gametophytic growth phase, moss gametophores superficially resemble sporophytes of vascular plants. Gametophores are differentiated into "leaves," "stems," and rhizoids (Fig. 12-8c). Moss rhizoids are multicellular filamentous structures with oblique septa. They serve to attach the gametophores to the substrate.

There is considerable variation in the degree of complexity of the moss stem. Most stems have a central strand of elongate, presumably water-conducting cells. In many mosses (such as *Mnium,* in Fig. 12-9) this is a simple strand of relatively few cells. The complexity of stem anatomy of robust mosses (such as *Polytrichum*) approaches that of vascular plants. In *Polytrichum,* water-conducting, food-conducting, and strengthening elements have been identified. Lignin is lacking. However, development and relationship of form to function of moss stems has been little explored. Leaves of mosses are relatively small and usually possess a midrib, composed of elongate cells. Except in a few mosses, such as *Polytrichum,* the midrib is not continous with the central strand of the stem.

Up to this point, our discussion has been limited to vegetative growth. The gametophore (literally, "gamete bearer") ultimately gives rise to sexual structures. Depending on the species, archegonia and antheridia develop at the apex of either the main stem or short lateral branches. Mosses are either unisexual or bisexual. In some bisexual mosses, archegonia and antheridia develop on the same apex; in others, such as *Mnium* and *Funaria,* they develop on separate branches. *Polytrichum* is an example of a unisexual moss.

Antheridia and archegonia are multicellular structures, and each has a jacket of protective cells (Fig. 12-12a, c). During development, the interior antheridial cells divide mitotically to produce a large number of small cells. Each nucleus, with very little cytoplasm, then develops into a sperm. During sperm development, the individual chromosomes become compacted and appressed together, so that individual chromosomes cannot be discerned, and the nuclear material elongates to form the body of the sperm. Two flagella then form on the anterior end of the sperm (Fig. 12-12b). A single nonmotile egg develops in the base of the archegonium. The egg possesses a large haploid nucleus and a large amount of cytoplasm with abundant food reserve.

Water is necessary for fertilization. When water is present (even a thin film will suffice), male gametes are discharged and swim to the egg retained in the

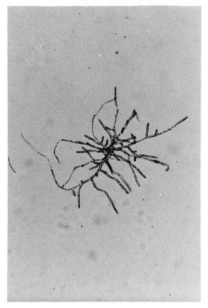

(a)

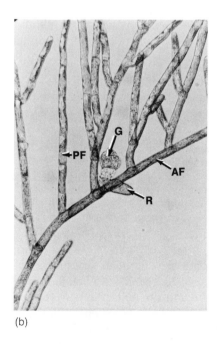

(b)

**Figure 12-8.** Gametophyte development of *Funaria hygrometrica.* (a) Development of the protonemal mat. (b) Gametophore initiation. Note axial filament (AF) from which develop photosynthetic filaments (PF), gametophores (G), and rhizoids (R). (c) Older gametophore (G), with leaf (L) and stem (S), is one cell removed from the axial filament (AF). Rhizoid (R) is also present.

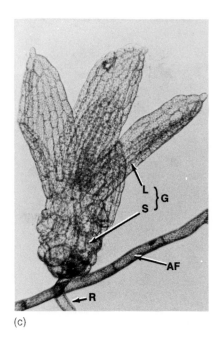

(c)

base of the archegonium. It appears that either the archegonium or the egg gives off a substance that attracts sperm. Laboratory studies have shown that moss sperm are attracted to sucrose (cane sugar) but not to other tested substances. Liverwort sperm, on the other hand, are attracted to albumin (protein), and not to sucrose. It is not known, however, whether sucrose is the specific moss-sperm attractant in nature.

Gamete fusion occurs soon after the sperm comes in contact with the egg. The sperm moves across the egg plasma membrane, migrates through the cytoplasm, and comes in contact with the nucleus. Although more than one sperm may enter the egg cytoplasm (*polyspermy*), only one fuses with the egg nucleus. The other sperm degenerate.

Zygote germination and early sporophyte development occur surrounded by maternal tissue of the archegonium. Embryo development is usually quite rapid. The embryo foot grows down into gametophytic tissue, apparently facilitating movement of nutrients from the haploid to the young diploid plant. The other end of the embryo grows upward, stretching the confining archegonium wall, which has increased in cell number. Ultimately, the wall is ruptured, the upper part of the archegonium being carried aloft like a cap on top of the elongating sporophyte (Fig. 12-12d). Even though broken away from the archegonium base, the cap—called a *calyptra* (kalyptra = a covering for the head)—undergoes a limited amount of growth and differentiation.

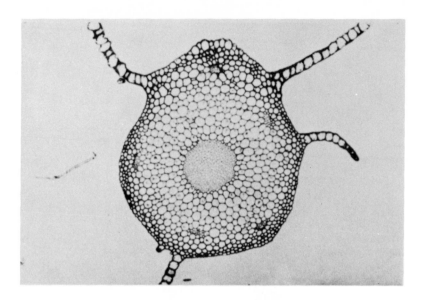

**Figure 12-9.** Transection of a gametophore stem of *Mnium*. Note the central cylinder of (elongate) cells of small diameter.

The calyptra is not a passive structure. It exerts considerable influence on subsequent sporophyte development, and has a very important morphogenetic effect on capsule differentiation. The young sporophyte is a needle-shaped structure. During sporophyte growth, cells at the calyptra tip form a tight mechanical enclosure around the sporophyte apex. As long as the calyptra is intact and pressure on the apex is maintained, the capsule does not develop. This has been indicated by results of experimental studies in which premature removal of the calyptra resulted in precocious capsule development. Capsule inhibition, at least in older sporophytes, is due to mechanical restraint and not to hormonal control. When the calyptra is removed, the cells killed, and the calyptra replaced, no capsule develops. It is also possible to prevent capsule development by replacing the calyptra with a tight-fitting piece of tinfoil or similar pressure device. Additional research is needed on the influence of both mechanical and chemical factors on sporophyte growth and capsule initiation and differentiation.

The form of the mature sporophyte is well adapted for its function, which is the production and discharge of spores. Capsules of most mosses are borne on top of an elongate seta. This is a distinct adaptive advantage for wind dispersal of spores. The capsule itself is usually differentiated into three general regions: one region for photosynthesis, one for spore production, and one for spore dispersal. The basal part of the capsule, continuous with the seta, is specialized for photosynthesis. Stomata are present, and adjacent tissue contains abundant chloroplasts (Fig. 12-10b).

The central capsule region is specialized for spore formation and development. The most important feature of this region is the presence of sporogenous tissue composed of cells that undergo meiosis. The exact relationship between sporogenous tissue and surrounding nonsporogenous tissue is variable, depending on the species. One pattern is shown in Fig. 12-10 in both cross and longitudinal sections. The diploid nucleus in each cell of the sporogenous tissue undergoes meiosis to form four haploid nuclei, thereby re-establishing the haploid condition. A wall then forms around each nucleus and adjacent cytoplasm to form a haploid spore. Spore walls of land plants in general are impregnated with waxy compounds. These compounds are amazingly resistant to degradation, so spores are well represented in the fossil record.

Whereas the middle portion of the capsule is involved in spore production, the apical region is modified to facilitate spore discharge. A lid, or *operculum*, develops on the anterior end of the capsule (Fig. 12-11a). When the capsule is mature, the operculum falls away. Loss of the operculum, however, does not usually expose the spores, because most mosses have a structure called a *peristome* (peri = all round; stoma = mouth) (Fig. 12-11b, c) directly under the operculum. The peristome is composed of teeth-like units, the number and form of which depend on the species. Peristome teeth generally are *hygroscopic* (moving in response to changes in relative humidity). In most mosses, tips of the teeth are free. The free teeth (such in as *Mnium*) flick out spores by bending in and out of the capsule mouth in response to changes in humidity. Peristome teeth of other mosses may be joined at the tips. In these plants, the teeth may be hygroscopic (*Funaria*) or rigid (*Polytrichum*). (It is of interest that lignin has been found in the peristome teeth of *Polytrichum*.) Spores of these plants sift out through openings between adjacent teeth. Peristome teeth hinder the rate of spore discharge, thus providing for dispersal over a longer period of time. However, many mosses that lack peristome teeth are distributed just as well as those that have them. Wind and water are the two most important agents of spore dispersal. Spores of a few mosses, such as those of coprophilous species of *Splachnum*, are insect-disseminated. The life cycle of a moss is diagrammed in Fig. 12-12.

With perhaps one exception (*Buxbaumia*), sporophytes of mosses (and other bryophytes) are permanently attached to the gametophyte. How, then, are sporophytes nourished? The young moss embryo is nonphotosynthetic, and like most plant and animal embryos, moss embryos are nutritionally parasitic on surrounding tissue. However, most moss sporophytes soon develop chloro-

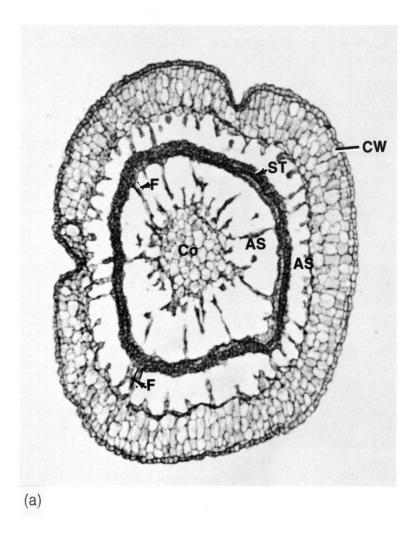

(a)

**Figure 12-10.** Sporophyte capsule of *Polytrichum*. (a) Young capsule in cross section, showing capsule wall (CW), air spaces (AS), sporogenous tissue (ST), and columella (Co). The sporogenous tissue is held in place by filaments (F) that extend across the air spaces. (b) Nearly mature capsule in longisection. Note operculum (O), capsule wall (CW), columella (Co), spores (S), and region with stomata (St).

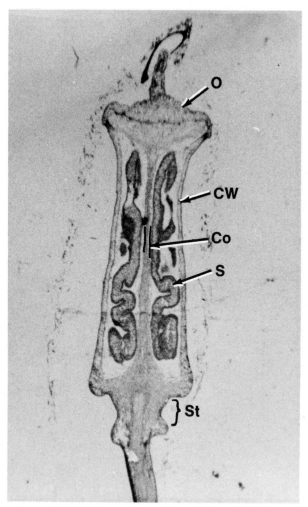

(b)

(a)

(b)

**Figure 12-11.** Moss capsules. (a) *Polytrichum juniperinum*. The operculum (O) still covers the capsule apex. (b) *Funaria hygrometrica*. The 16 teeth (T), the tips of which are united, rotate in response to humidity changes. (c) *Tortula mucronifolia*. Spores sift out between the twisted teeth tips.

(c)

plasts and subsequently store abundant starch. Analysis has shown that sporophytes possess the same photosynthetic pigments (chlorophylls *a* and *b*) as gametophytes. Quantitatively, they may possess a higher concentration of these pigments. A recent study on two mosses has shown that the sporophyte of *Funaria* is photosynthetically independent, whereas the sporophyte of *Polytrichum*, on the other hand, is dependent on the gametophyte for a large part of its carbohydrates. All moss sporophytes obtain water and minerals, and perhaps other compounds, from the gametophytes.

The form of the sporophyte contrasts sharply with that of the gametophyte. The sporophyte lacks leaves and rhizoids and does not branch. Experimental studies have shown that the characteristic form of the sporophyte is not a necessary consequence of the diploid condition. Severed from the foot and capsule and placed on a suitable medium, it is possible to induce seta cells to divide. However, cell division and differentiation do not result in development of new sporophytic parts. Instead, the diploid seta cells give rise to protonemal filaments. Cells are somewhat larger, but otherwise the filaments are identical to those derived from haploid spores. Moreover, diploid gametophores develop from diploid protonema, and gametes produced are also diploid. Fusion of diploid gametes results in the formation of a sporophyte that is tetraploid. This is twice the number of chromosomes that are present in a normal sporophytic plant. From this type of study it is evident that the number of

**Bryophytes**

chromosomes in the nucleus does not explain the morphological differences between gametophytic and sporophytic generations. We must look elsewhere for an explanation of the basis of alternation of heteromorphic generations found in mosses and other embryophytes.

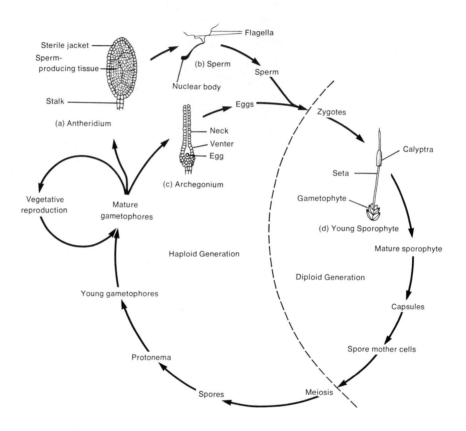

**Figure 12-12.** Life cycle of a moss.

# 13

## Ferns and
## Fern Allies

The ferns and fern allies include the ferns, psilopsids, lycopsids, and horse-tails (sphenopsids). These are seedless, vascular plants. They have an alternation of generations in which the sporophyte is dominant and has an axis containing xylem and phloem. (Further information concerning details of organ and tissue differentiation of vascular plants, with particular reference to seed plants, can be found in Salisbury and Parke, *Vascular Plants: Form and Function*, this series.) The ferns and fern allies differ from each other primarily in the pattern of organization of the plant body. A little of this diversity, with emphasis on contemporary representatives, is discussed in the following pages.

### Psilopsids

The psilopsids (class Psilopsida) form a small group of vascular plants including several genera of fossil and two genera of contemporary plants. The plants are relatively simple, often consisting of branched, underground *rhizomes* (underground stems) from which aerial axes arise. Roots are absent; the rhizomes are attached to the substrate by unicellular rhizoids. Leaves are also absent (psilos = bare), although the stem often has lateral appendages or emergences that lack vascular traces. The Devonian *Rhynia,* from Scotland, is one of the simplest of the fossil psilopsids (Fig. 13-1).

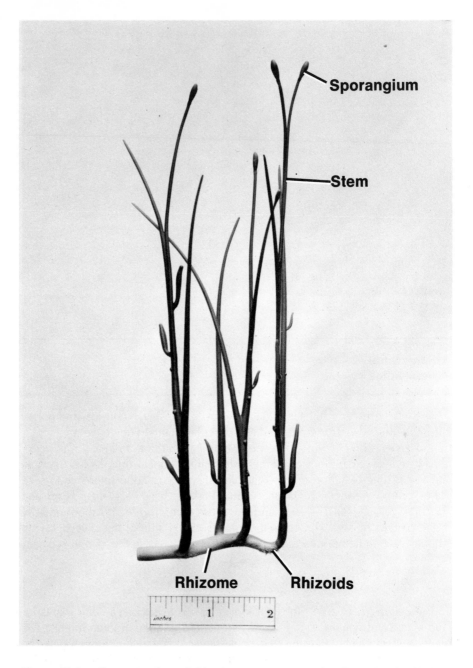

**Figure 13-1.** Reconstruction of *Rhynia gwynne-vaughanii,* a Devonian fossil plant. Courtesy of the Field Museum of Natural History, Chicago, Illinois.

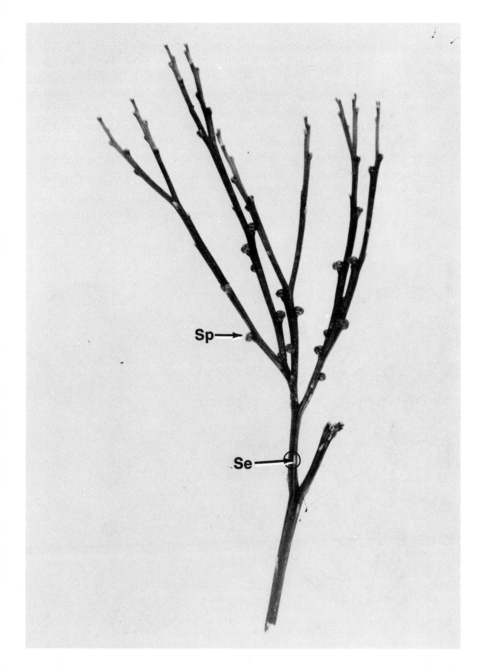

**Figure 13-2.** *Psilotum nudum.* The dichotomously branched aerial axis bears scale-like emergences (SE) and sporangia (Sp).

---

*Psilotum* (Fig. 13-2) is the best known living psilopsid. It is a relatively small plant (up to 61 cm in height) of the tropics and subtropics and is readily grown in the greenhouse. The erect, branched axis arises from an underground rhizome. The bulk of its photosynthesis occurs in the green stem with the green, scale-like emergences forming a very small part of the photosynthetic area of the plant. Internally, the stem axis is simple. It consists of a central core of xylem, irregular in outline, with associated phloem, that is surrounded by a broad cortex (Fig. 13-3). The outer region of the cortex contains the photosynthetic chlorenchyma and an extensive air space system that has continuity with the external atmosphere through stomata (also called stomates). This provides for an efficient gas exchange system in the stem.

The sporangia are borne laterally on the stem in the axils of the appendages.

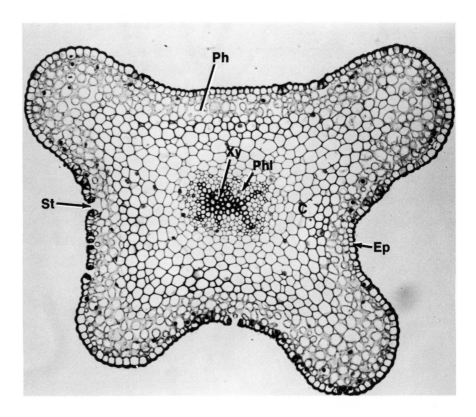

**Figure 13-3.** Stem cross section of *Psilotum nudum*. Stoma (St); photosynthetic tissue (Ph); cortex (C); epidermis (Ep); phloem (Phl); and xylem (Xy).

Meiosis occurs in the sporangium prior to spore formation, and the spores upon germination give rise to bisexual gametophytes. The gametophytes are subterranean, lack chlorophyll, and are always associated with an endophytic fungus. The sperm are multiflagellate, and the flagella are all of the whiplash type characteristic of green plants.

How close a relationship exists between *Psilotum* (and *Tmesipteris*, the other living psilopsid) to the fossil psilopsids is unclear. There is no evidence from the fossil record that the psilopsids survived beyond the beginning of the Carboniferous; we find a complete gap in the fossil record past the Devonian. Whether the contemporary psilopsids are, in fact, psilopsids hopefully will be determined by current and future research.

### Lycopsids

The class name Lycopsida stems from *Lycopodium,* a living genus of the group. Fossils similar to *Lycopodium* have been described from Carboniferous strata. As a group, the lycopsids have a fossil record extending back to the early Devonian. A luxuriant and diverse lycopsid flora of both herbaceous and arborescent forms occurred in the Carboniferous coal swamp forests. Reduction of lycopsid diversity during the Permian accompanied the decrease in extent of the swamps during that period. Although widespread in the tropics and temperate regions, only five genera of herbaceous lycopsids survive.

The following combination of characteristics serves to distinguish the lycopsids from the other vascular plants. The leaves are vascularized by a single, unbranched (with very few exceptions) midvein. The strand of xylem that extends into the leaf (called a *leaf trace*) does not leave a gap where it departs from the xylem of the stem. Finally, the sporangia are borne near or in the leaf axils, or on the upper (*adaxial*) surface of a subtending appendage called a *sporophyll.*

*Lycopodium* and *Selaginella* (Fig. 13-4) are two of the more common lycopsids. They both have the same general geographic range and the same general pattern of growth. The aerial portion is usually highly branched and is clothed by numerous small, green leaves. Roots arise scattered along a horizontal stem. Stem anatomy is relatively simple, often not much more complex than that of *Psilotum.* The vascular system in *Lycopodium* consists of a central strand of xylem tissue, which may be dissected in some species (Fig. 13-5a). In *Selaginella* two or more separate vascular systems may be present in the stem (a condition known as *polystely*) (Fig. 13-5b). The sporangia in both genera are aggregated into cones called *strobili,* or are scattered along the stem.

In *Lycopodium* all of the spores formed by the plant are of the same shape and size (Fig. 13-6a), and the plants are said to be homosporous (homo = one and the same). (Bryophytes and psilopsids are also homosporous plants.)

Strobilus

Rhizome

Root

(a)

**Figure 13-4.** (a) *Lycopodium.* (b) *Selaginella.* (a) Courtesy of the Field Museum of Natural History, Chicago, Illinois.

Germination of spores of *Lycopodium* results in the development of bisexual gametophytes that grow at the soil surface and have chlorophyll, or that are subterranean and nongreen. In both cases, the gametophyte is associated with an endophytic fungus (recalling the mycorrhizal relationship described earlier).

A different situation appears in *Selaginella.* Here, two types of sporangia develop on the same plant (Fig. 13-6b). One type of sporangia produces a few large spores that upon germination give rise to female gametophytes. Because

(b)

the spores are large, the sporangium is called a *megasporangium* (megas = great), the spore a *megaspore*, and the female gametophyte a *megagametophyte*. Many smaller spores develop in the other sporangial type, and these spores give rise to male gametophytes. The sporangium in which these spores develop is called a *microsporangium* (mikros = small), the spore a *microspore*, and the male gametophyte a *microgametophyte*. Plants that form spores of two morphological types are called *heterosporous* (heteros = other) plants.

In *Selaginella* (as in heterosporous plants in general), most of the development of the gametophyte occurs within the confines of the spore coat. There is a marked reduction in the extent of development of gametophytes of heterosporous plants, compared to gametophytes of homosporous plants. The microgametophyte of *Selaginella* consists of little more than a single antheridium, and the megagametophyte consists of a few archegonia embedded in a small pad of tissue. The reduction in extent of vegetative development of the gametophytic generations has been carried even further in seed plants. In these plants, the mature pollen grain represents the microgametophyte, and the megagametophyte is retained within the ovule of the parental plant (see Salisbury and Parke, *Vascular Plants: Form and Function*, this series). Resemblance to the seed condition is found in some species of *Selaginella* in which the megaspore

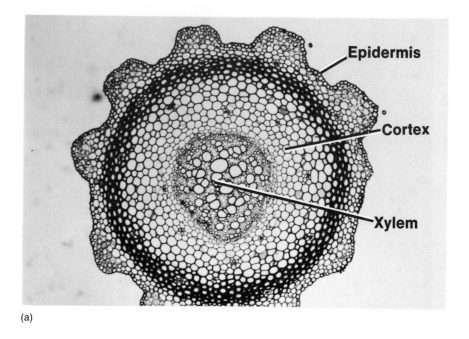

(a)

**Figure 13-5.** (a) Stem cross section of *Lycopodium cernuum*. The xylem forms a single central strand. (b) Stem cross section of *Selaginella* sp. Two separate vascular cylinders (X) are surrounded by an air space (AS). Filaments that hold the vascular cylinders in position are not intact in this sectioned material.

may be retained in the dehisced sporangium, and in which megagametophyte development and fertilization may thus occur surrounded by parental tissue. Some of the Paleozoic lycopsids (e.g., *Lepidocarpon*) more closely approached the seed condition. (See Doyle, Suggestions for Further Reading, for a discussion of homospory, heterospory, and evolution of the seed.)

*Isoetes* is a heterosporous lycopsid of relatively wide distribution in temperate climates, where it often grows in the margins of marshes and ponds. This plant, called quillwort, resembles an onion or chive in its general form. The plant body of *Isoetes* consists of numerous strap-shaped leaves that are attached to the apex of a very short, often subterranean, stem, and the roots arise from the basal part of the stem. *Isoetes* also differs from *Lycopodium* and *Selaginella* in that it undergoes a small amount of secondary growth.

### Sphenopsids

The sphenopsids (class Sphenopsida) are like the lycopsids in that they reached maximum development (in both size and diversity) during the Carbon-

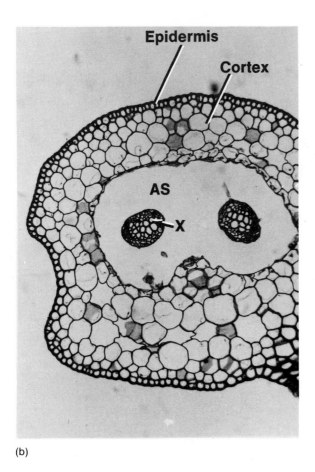

**Epidermis**

**Cortex**

AS

X

(b)

iferous, were conspicuous components of the coal swamp forests, and declined rapidly with the drying up of the swamps during the Permian. Today only a single genus, *Equisetum,* with twenty-five to thirty species, survives. The class name *Sphenopsida* derives from the Carboniferous herbaceous plant, *Spheno-phyllum* (sphen = wedge-shaped, referring to the wedge-shaped leaves of this plant).

Sphenopsids are characterized by leaves borne in whorls, giving the stem a distinctly jointed, or articulated, appearance. Another major definitive feature is the presence of sporangial-bearing structures called *sporangiophores.* Evidence in the fossil record and from ontogeny of contemporary plants indicates that the sporangiophore is not a leaflike structure (as is the lycopsid sporophyll); rather it appears to represent a highly modified small branch system.

*Equisetum* is nearly worldwide in distribution, but has greatest variety in the northern hemisphere. Some species are branched, others unbranched. The

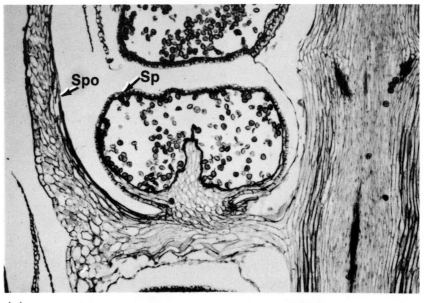

(a)

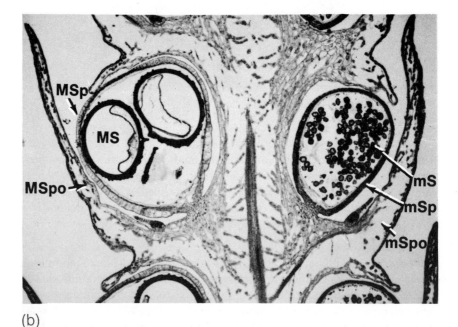

(b)

**Figure 13-6.** (a) Sporangium of the homosporous *Lycopodium*. The sporangium (Sp) occurs on the adaxial surface of the sporophyll (Spo). (b) Sporangia of the heterosporous *Selaginella.* Note megaspore (MS), megasporangium (MSp), megasporophyll (MSpo), microspores (mS), microsporangium (mSp), and microsporophyll (mSpo).

common name horsetail generally refers to the branched species, and the name scouring rush to the unbranched forms. As their name implies, some of the unbranched forms were occasionally used for scouring purposes, because they have large amounts of silica in the walls of some of their epidermal cells. The deposition of silica at specific places in the plant body is a feature of all species of *Equisetum*, although the amount present is variable. Silica uptake, transport, and deposition in *Equisetum* are virtually unexplored areas of research.

The aerial branches of *Equisetum* arise from underground, and often deep-seated, rhizomes (Fig. 13-7). The leaves, united laterally to form a sheath around the stem, are relatively unimportant organs for photosynthesis. As in *Psilotum*, most of the photosynthesis occurs in stem tissue specialized for this function. The small, scalelike leaves of some species are dead at maturity. Stem anatomy is noted for the large number of canals that extend the length of each internode (Fig. 13-8); the canals do not traverse the node, which is a solid diaphragm of tissue. Many plants that presently grow in wet or swampy places also have extensive internal air space systems, and the existence of a similar air canal system in *Equisetum* is thought to indicate that ancestors of *Equisetum* were plants of wet places. Fossils similar to *Equisetum* (called *Equisetites*) have been found in Cenozoic and Mesozoic strata as far back as the Triassic.

The sporangiophores are aggregated into *strobili* at the branch tips (Fig. 13-7). In some species (for example, *E. arvense* and *E. telmeteia*) the strobili develop on specialized, ephemeral, nonchlorophyllous branches. These branches usually develop from the rhizomes during the spring and summer, but remain underground during the winter. The specialized branches elongate, and the spores are discharged during the early spring. The strobili develop at apices of the normal, photosynthetic branches in species like *E. hiemale* and *E. laevigatum*. All species of *Equisetum* are homosporous, but the spores are unique among extant plants in the possession of appendages called *elaters* that curl and uncurl in response to changes in humidity. It is assumed that this motion aids in spore discharge from the sporangium. Elater uncurling during drying might also aid spore dispersal by retarding the rate of fall after discharge. (The latter suggestion could be measured experimentally.)

The photosynthetic gametophytes are easily grown in culture by sowing spores from a freshly-discharging sporangium on moist soil or on a simple inorganic medium solidified with agar. In crowded cultures, some plants bear only antheridia, whereas others bear only archegonia. This is a nutritional response resulting from crowded conditions, and not true unisexualism, as is shown by experiments in which individual spores are isolated and the gametophytes grown separately. Most of the species thus tested have been found to have bisexual gametophytes. The relatively large multiflagellate sperm (Fig. 13-9) are capable of fertilizing the egg of the same gametophyte.

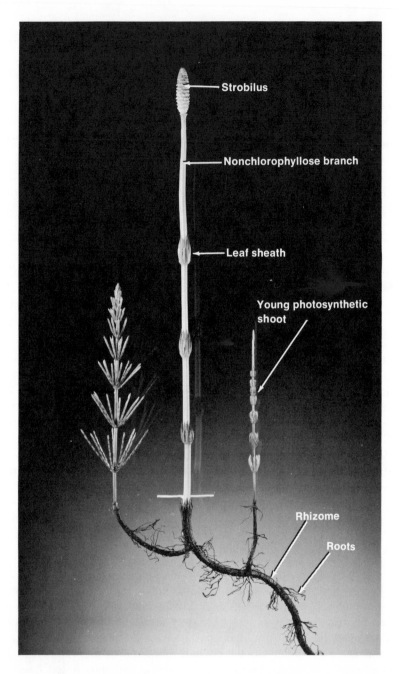

**Figure 13-7.** Reconstruction of *Equisetum arvense*. Courtesy of the Field Museum of Natural History, Chicago, Illinois.

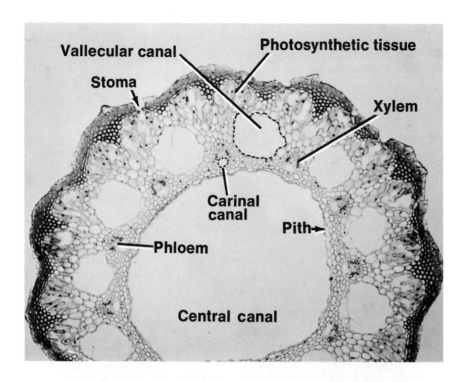

## Chapter 13

**Figure 13-8.** Cross section of the stem of *Equisetum litorale*.

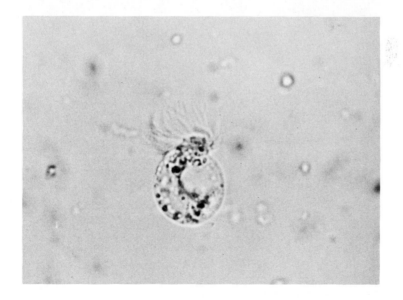

**Figure 13–9.** Multiflagellate sperm of *Equisetum laevigatum*. Note the relatively large amount of cytoplasm.

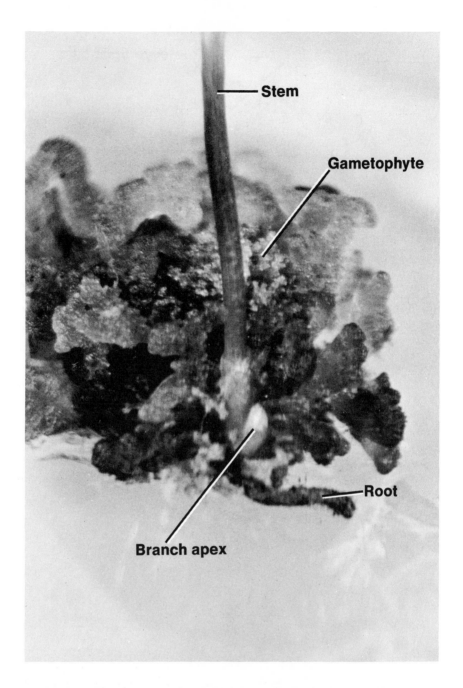

**Figure 13-10.** Gametophyte and young sporophyte of *Equisetum hiemale* grown in single spore culture. The first stem and first root, and the apex of the second aerial branch are visible. Note also the irregular growth habit of the gametophyte.

The young sporophyte (Fig. 13-10) has the same general organization as the adult plant. The rhizome develops during later growth.

### Ferns

The ferns, or Pteropsida (pteris = ferns), are the only group of vascular plants discussed in this book which have many contemporary genera and species. Ferns have a long geologic history, extending back into the Devonian. (Many of the plants with fernlike foliage of the Devonian and Carboniferous, however, were not ferns, but seed plants.)

The definitive features of ferns are large leaves, a leaf gap where the leaf trace leaves the vascular system of the stem, and the development of sporangia on specialized leaf segments, or on the margin or lower (*abaxial*) surface of the leaf.

The leaf (or frond, as it is often called) is the most conspicuous part of most fern plants (Fig. 13-11). The form of the leaf is quite variable, and this variation is prized by gardeners and florists, besides being of interest to morphogeneticists. In some, the leaf margin is entire, but it is generally dissected into leaflets called *pinnae*. The pinnae, in turn, may be further subdivided.

The leaf arises from either a rhizome or an erect stem that has shortened internodes (Fig. 13-11). (Only the tree ferns have stems that grow to any height.) Cell enlargement on the adaxial surface of the leaf occurs at a greater rate than on the abaxial surface. This results in a characteristic curling of the young leaf, somewhat like that of a fiddlehead (Fig. 13-11a). Uncurling of the leaf during leaf expansion occurs when the rate of enlargement of cells on the abaxial leaf surface increases. This curled pattern of leaf development, a feature of most ferns and some cycads (gymnospermous seed plants), is called *circinate vernation*.

The vascular system of the stem and rhizome (Fig. 13-12) is well developed and often quite complex because of the presence of leaf gaps. (Description of the variation will not be given here; the interested student should refer to the book by Foster and Gifford, cited in Suggestions for Further Reading, for this information.)

Sporangia, as mentioned earlier, develop embedded in modified leaf segments or on the margins or abaxial surface of leaves. The sporangia are often grouped into *sori* (singular sorus) (soros = a heap), and the sori may be protected by an outgrowth of leaf tissue called an *indusium* (Fig. 13-13). Occasionally, as in the maidenhair fern (*Adiantum*), an infolded leaf margin, called a *false indusium,* covers the sporangia. The position of the sporangium on the leaf, and the form of the indusium, when present, are important in fern classification.

---

(a)

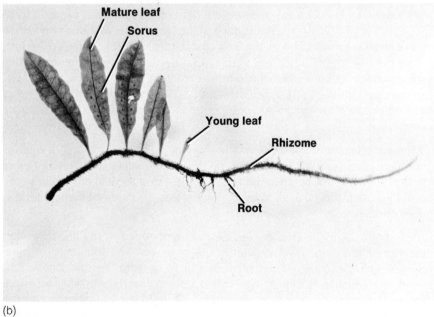

(b)

**Figure 13-11.** (a) *Polystichum setiferum*. The leaves arise from a short, erect stem. Note circinate vernation of the young leaves. (b) *Polypodium lycopodioides*. The leaves of this plant arise scattered along a rhizome. The older leaves bear sporangia aggregated into sori.

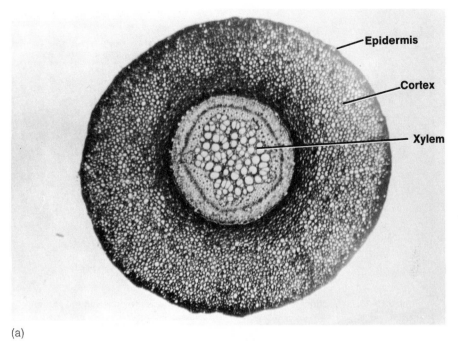

(a)

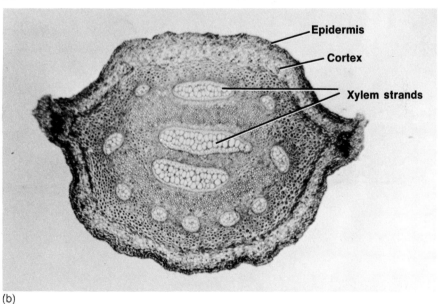

(b)

**Figure 13-12.** (a) Rhizome cross section of *Gleichenia* showing the relatively simple arrangement of the vascular system. (b) Rhizome cross section of *Pteridium* showing the more complex vascular system of this plant.

---

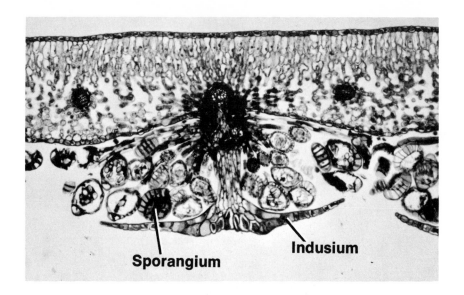

**Figure 13-13.** Section of *Cyrtomium* leaf to show indusium covering the sorus.

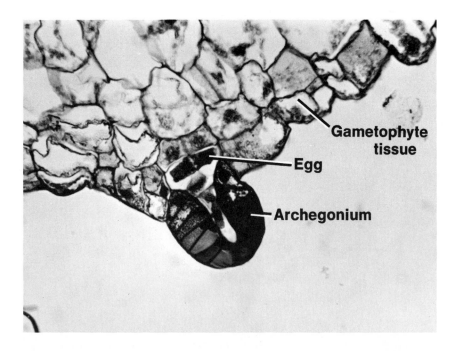

**Figure 13-14.** An old fern archegonium, the base of which is embedded in midrib tissue. The archegonium (and antheridia, not shown) are borne on the ventral surface of the prothallus.

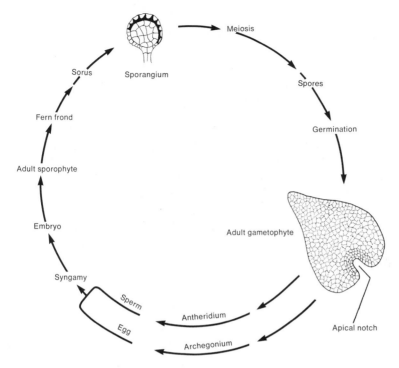

**Figure 13-15.** Life cycle of a fern.

The gametophyte (called a *prothallus* in fern terminology) of many ferns is dorsiventrally flattened and heart-shaped. It is anchored to the substrate by colorless, unicellular rhizoids, and the antheridia and archegonia are borne on the lower surface of the prothallus. The antheridia are often scattered among the rhizoids in the posterior portion of the prothallus; the archegonia are partially embedded in midrib tissue behind the apical notch (Fig. 13-14). The sperm are multiflagellate and resemble those of *Equisetum* (Fig. 13-9). The life cycle of a fern is diagrammed in Fig. 13-15.

## Summary of Green Plants

| Photosynthetic Pigments | Flagella | Food Reserve |
|---|---|---|
| Chlorophyll *a* | Generally 2 (or more) | True starch |
| Chlorophyll *b* | Whiplash | |

*Additional:* eukaryotic cellular structure; cellulose in cell wall; cell division by centripetal ingrowth of septum or by floating cell-plate.

## Evolutionary Relationships of Chlorophyta

Many botanists believe that there is a close phenetic (see Classification, Chapter 1) relationship between the green algae and the land plants. Their similarity in pigmentation (chlorophylls *a* and *b*), food reserve (true starch stored within chloroplasts), and flagellation (whiplash flagella, when present), in addition to other characteristics not discussed in this book, indicates the occurrence of similar morphological and physiological attributes, and therefore similar biochemical pathways. In my view, the green algae and the embryophytes form a natural and distinct group of organisms and are here placed in the same taxon, the division Chlorophyta.

Moreover, many botanists believe that the primitive land plants arose from early green algal stock, that these two plant groups have a close phylogenetic relationship. However, there are missing links in this presumed phylogenetic sequence. Fossil forms that are intermediate in morphological and structural complexity between green algae and land plants have not yet been identified. Without this information the specific group of green algae that was ancestral to the land plants cannot be known with certainty. Of course, absence of fossils from the geologic record might be explained in a variety of ways. It does not necessarily mean that these organisms did not exist. Because of their relatively small size and lack of hard parts, green algae are not good material for fossilization.

Other kinds of evidence, therefore, must be used to discover which stock group is most likely ancestral to green land plants. In the green algal order Ulotrichales (which includes *Ulothrix, Pleurococcus, Fritschiella, Ulva,* and *Enteromorpha*), there is great morphological and physiological diversity—the type of diversity that gives insight into how land plants might have evolved. Species of ulotrichalean algae consist of unicells, unbranched or branched filaments, or of parenchyma. Some filamentous species are highly differentiated, having prostrate systems from which arise numerous branched photosynthetic filaments and rhizoidal filaments that penetrate the substratum. This type of development recalls the early gametophyte (protonema) development of mosses. In this respect, *Fritschiella* (Fig. 13-16) is of particular interest because it not only possesses an erect, prostrate, and rhizoidal system (the heterotrichous habit of growth), but it also grows on mud. *Fritschiella* is a contemporary green algal land plant. The habitat of *Pleurococcus* also is noteworthy in that it shows that ulotrichalean green algae can survive in a terrestrial environment without formation of specialized resistant cells.

In summary, we find that the extant ulotrichalean green algae exhibit considerable morphological diversity as a group. Some are strictly aquatic organisms, others exhibit at least partial adaptation to a land environment, and one normally lives in a terrestrial habitat. The discovery that *Fritschiella* undergoes cell division by floating cell-plate formation (Fig. 13-17) further bridges the gap between green algae and land plants. For these reasons, it is believed that land plants evolved from an early stock of ulotrichalean green algae. This concept is diagrammatically represented in Fig. 13-18. This representation is an oversimplification, but it graphically illustrates the justifications for the belief that

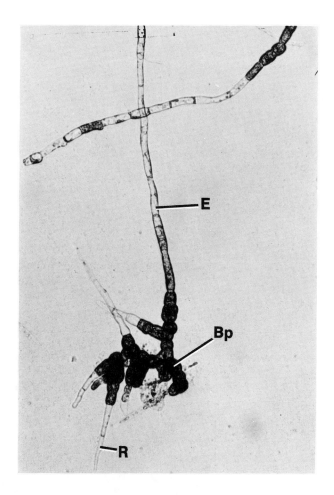

**Figure 13-16.** Habit of the green alga *Fritschiella tuberosus* grown in culture, showing erect system (E), basal parenchyma (Bp), and rhizoid (R). Courtesy of Dr. G. McBride, University of Michigan, Ann Arbor.

land plants are genetically related to green algae. A discussion of the relationship of the several groups of land plants to each other, and whether the land plants evolved from a single algal ancestor (monophyletic origin of land plants) or different groups of land plants evolved from separate green algal ancestors (polyphyletic origin) is beyond the scope of this book. Regardless of manner of origin, the land plants are the most important to man economically. The seed plants are man's staff of life. Much of man's understanding of life's processes, however, has been, and will continue to be, obtained by studying the non-seed plants.

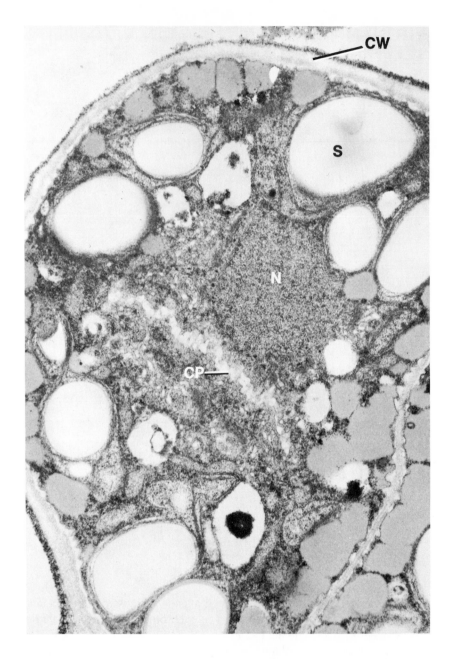

**Figure 13-17.** Electronmicrograph of *Fritschiella tuberosus,* showing floating cell plate (CP) characteristic of land plants. Also labelled is the nucleus (N), starch (S) in the chloroplasts, and the cell wall (CW). Courtesy of Dr. G. McBride, University of Michigan, Ann Arbor.

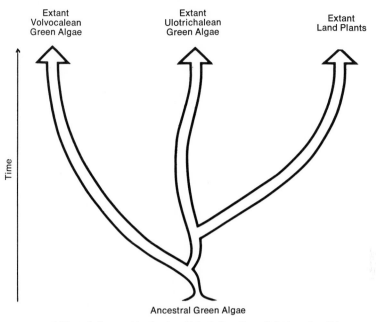

Extant
Volvocalean
Green Algae

Extant
Ulotrichalean
Green Algae

Extant
Land Plants

Time

Ancestral Green Algae

(chlorophylls *a* and *b,* starch, whiplash flagella, cellulosic cell walls)

**Figure 13-18.**    Presumed phylogenetic origin of land plants from green algae.

# Appendix

**Appendix Table 1.** Summary of attributes of major groups of photosynthetic plants

| Plant Group | Photosynthetic Pigments | Carbohydrate Food Reserve | Flagellation |
|---|---|---|---|
| Cyanophyta (blue-green algae) | chlorophyll *a* phycobiliproteins | glycogen | none |
| Rhodophyta (red algae) | chlorophyll *a* ± chlorophyll *d* phycobiliproteins | floridean starch | none |
| Chrysophyta (golden algae and diatoms) | chlorophyll *a* chlorophyll *c* fucoxanthin | chryso- laminarin | one whiplash, one tinsel; anterior insertion |
| Phaeophyta (brown algae) | chlorophyll *a* chlorophyll *c* fucoxanthin | laminarin | one whiplash, one tinsel; lateral insertion |
| Pyrrophyta (dinoflagellates) | chlorophyll *a* chlorophyll *c* | true starch? | one whiplash (trailing), one tinsel (girdling); lateral or apical insertion |
| Xanthophyta (yellow-green algae) | chlorophyll *a* | chryso- laminarin | one whiplash, one tinsel; anterior insertion |
| Euglenophyta (euglenoids) | chlorophyll *a* chlorophyll *b* | paramylon | one or more tinsel; anterior insertion |
| Chlorophyta (green algae and land plants) | chlorophyll *a* chlorophyll *b* | true starch | one or more whiplash; anterior insertion |

Additional details about carbohydrate food reserves follow. However, note should be made that this information is derived from studies on relatively few organisms. The biochemistry and biology of algal reserve polysaccharides (and oils) is a largely unexplored field and awaits further investigation.

**Green plant (true) starch:** This is a mixture of two glucose polymers, *amylose* and *amylopectin*. Amylose is exclusively unbranched, containing between 200 to 1,000 glucose units with $\alpha$-(1→4)-glucosyl linkages. Its molecular weight varies from 10,000 to 100,000. Amylopectin is very highly branched with unit chain lengths of 20 to 25. The chains have $\alpha$-(1→4)-glucosyl linkages, with $\alpha$-(1→6)-glucosyl linkages at branch points. The molecular weight of amylopectin varies from 50,000 to 1,000,000.

The starch grain, at least of flowering plants, consists of about 25 per cent amylose and 75 per cent amylopectin. *Spirogyra* starch contains about 20 per cent amylose and 80 per cent amylopectin.

**Glycogen:** Glycogen is a very highly branched molecule with $\alpha$-(1→4)- glucosyl linkages and $\alpha$-(1→6)-glucosyl linkages at branch points. The lengths of the main chain are variable. In *Oscillatoria* it consists of 14 to 16 glucose residues, and of 11 to 13 residues in many animals.

**Floridean starch:** In red algae (for example, in *Rhodymenia*), the floridean starch is devoid of any amylose (unbranched) component. It has $\alpha$-(1→4)-glucosyl linkages, with $\alpha$-(1→6)-glucosyl linkages at branch points. The average chain length contains about 15 glucose molecules, and it is less highly branched than glycogen.

**Laminarin:** Laminarin has chain lengths of about 20 glucose molecules. The chains have $\beta$-(1→3)-glucosyl linkages. There is a very low degree of branching, with $\beta$-(1→6)-glucosyl linkages at branch points. A small portion of the chains are terminated with a molecule of mannitol.

**Chrysolaminarin:** Chrysolaminarin (leucosin) has short chain lengths, about 8 glucose units. Otherwise it is similar to laminarin, except that mannitol is absent.

**Paramylon:** Paramylon is an exclusively unbranched molecule of $\beta$-(1→3)-linked glucose residues. The individual molecules vary considerably in their degrees of polymerization.

**Appendix Table 2.** Fossil record of main groups of plants

| Era | Period | | Green algae | Bryophytes | Psilopsids | Lycopsids | Sphenopsids | Ferns | Gymnosperms | Angiosperms |
|---|---|---|---|---|---|---|---|---|---|---|
| Cenozoic | Quaternary | 1* | | | | | | | | |
| | Tertiary | 63 | | | | | | | | |
| Mesozoic | Cretaceous | 135 | | | ? | | | | | |
| | Jurassic | 180 | | | | | | | | |
| | Triassic | 230 | | | ? | | | | | |
| Paleozoic | Permian | 280 | | | | | | | | |
| | Carboniferous — Pennsylvanian | 310 | | | | | | | | |
| | Carboniferous — Mississippian | 345 | | | | | | | | |
| | Devonian | 405 | | | | | | | | |
| | Silurian | 425 | | | | | | | | |
| | Ordovician | 500 | | | | | | | | |
| | Cambrian | 600 | | | | | | | | |
| Precambrian | Late Precambrian | 1,200 | ? | | | | | | | |
| | Middle Precambrian | 2,500 | | | | | | | | |
| | Early Precambrian | 4,500 – 5,000 ? | | | | | | | | |

*The numbers indicate the beginning of the period in millions of years.

# Appendix Table 3.  Fossil record of main groups of green plants

| Era | Period | | Schizophyta | Eumycota | Myxomycota | Cyanophyta | Rhodophyta | Chrysophyta | Phaeophyta | Pyrrophyta | Xanthophyta | Euglenophyta | Chlorophyta |
|---|---|---|---|---|---|---|---|---|---|---|---|---|---|
| Cenozoic | Quaternary | 1 * | | | ? | | | | | | | | |
| | Tertiary | 63 | | | | | | | | | | | |
| Mesozoic | Cretaceous | 135 | | | | | | | | | | | |
| | Jurassic | 180 | | | | | | | | | | | |
| | Triassic | 230 | | | | | | | | | | | |
| Paleozoic | Permian | 280 | | | | | | | | | | | |
| | Carboniferous — Pennsylvanian | 310 | | | | | | | ? | | | | |
| | Carboniferous — Mississippian | 345 | | | | | | | | | | | |
| | Devonian | 405 | | | | | | | | | | | |
| | Silurian | 425 | | | | | | | | | | | |
| | Ordovician | 500 | | | | | | | | | | | |
| | Cambrian | 600 | | | | | | | | | | | |
| Precambrian | Late Precambrian | 1,200 | | | | | | | | | | | ? |
| | Middle Precambrian | 2,500 | | | | | | | | | | | |
| | Early Precambrian | 4,500 – 5,000 ? | | | | | | | | | | | |

*The numbers indicate the beginning of the period in millions of years.

# Glossary

*Acetate algae.* A physiological group of algae that are unable to respire hexose sugars when cultured in the dark, but do respire short-chain carbohydrate molecules such as acetate.

*Achlorophyllous.* Without chlorophyll.

*Aeciospore.* A dikaryotic spore produced by rusts.

*Aecium.* Structure in which aeciospores are formed.

*Alternation of generations.* The alternation of a meiospore-producing, diploid growth phase with a gamete-producing, haploid growth phase in the life cycle of an organism.

*Amitosis.* Nuclear division without the formation of spindle fibers and distinct chromosomes.

*Anisogamy.* Sexual fusion in which flagellated gametes are of dissimilar size.

*Antheridium.* Unicellular or multicellular gametangium of plants in which sperm are produced.

*Apothecium.* An open, generally cup-shaped fruiting body of Ascomycetes.

*Archegonium.* Multicellular gametangium of plants in which an egg is produced.

*Ascocarp.* Ascus-bearing reproductive structure in Ascomycetes.

*Ascogonium.* Female gametangium in Ascomycetes.

*Ascospore.*   A spore formed in an ascus.

*Ascus* (pl. asci).   A sac-like structure of Ascomycetes in which nuclear fusion and meiosis occur and meiospores develop.

*Autoecious.*   Completing its life cycle on a single host species.

*Autotrophic.*   The ability to utilize light energy, or the energy derived from the oxidation of inorganic compounds, to drive synthetic reactions in the cell.

*Axenic.*   Having only one kind of organism present in a culture.

*Bacteriophage.*   A virus that infects bacteria.

*Basidiocarp.*   Basidium-bearing reproductive structure in Basidiomycetes.

*Basidiospore.*   A spore formed on a basidium.

*Basidium.*   A structure in Basidiomycetes in which nuclear fusion and meiosis occur and which (usually) produces four meiospores.

*Calyptra.*   Gametophytic tissue (derived from the upper part of the archegonium) carried aloft by and forming a covering over the apex of the developing sporophyte of a moss.

*Capsid.*   The protein coat of a virus.

*Capsule.*   In bryophytes, a multicellular meiospore-producing structure.

*Carbohydrate.*   An organic molecule containing carbon, hydrogen, and oxygen; the hydrogen and oxygen are in a 2:1 ratio.

*Carpogonium.*   Female gametangium in the red algae.

*Carposporophyte.*   Parasitic carpospore-producing structure that develops after fertilization in red algae.

*Chemoautotrophic.*   The ability to use energy derived from the oxidation of inorganic compounds for the synthesis of organic foods.

*Chromatic adaptation.*   Wavelength-induced change in cell pigments.

*Circinate vernation.*   The characteristic coiling of young fern leaves.

*Cleistothecium.*   A completely closed fruiting body of Ascomycetes.

*Coenocytic.*   Multinucleate and nonseptate.

*Coenozygote.*   A multinucleate zygote resulting from the union of two multinucleate gametangia.

*Coli-phage.*   A virus that infects *Escherichia coli.*

*Conceptacle.*   A cavity in *Fucus* and its relatives in which gametangia develop.

*Conidiophore.*   A specialized hypha that bears conidia.

*Conidium.*   A nonflagellated mitospore cut off sequentially from the tip or side of a hypha.

*Cortex.*   Tissue that lies inside the epidermis and outside the vascular tissue.

*Cuticle.*   A waxy coating characteristic of, but not restricted to, the epidermis of embryophyte sporophytes.

*Dichotomous.*   Division of an axis into two equal branches.

*Dikaryotic.*   Having paired nuclei, each usually derived from different parents.

*Dimorphism.* Having two different forms.

*Diploid.* Having two full chromosome complements per nucleus.

*Dorsiventral.* Flattened with dissimilar dorsal and ventral surfaces.

*Egg.* A nonmotile female gamete that can fuse with a sperm.

*Embryo.* A multicellular young organism, developed from the zygote, which is surrounded by female reproductive tissue.

*Endospore.* Type of bacterial spore formed within the cell.

*Epiphytes.* Organisms that live on the surface of living plants.

*Eukaryotic.* Possessing a true nucleus; more generally, having double unit membrane cell organelles such as nucleus, mitochondrion, and chloroplast.

*Eyespot.* Carotenoid-containing region of flagellated cells assumed to be involved in light-oriented responses of these organisms.

*Flagellum.* A whip-like appendage that generally serves to propel a motile cell.

*Foot.* In bryophytes, a specialized absorptive structure of the sporophyte, embedded in gametophytic tissue.

*Fruiting body.* In fungi and slime molds, any structure that contains or bears spores.

*Gametangium.* A unicellular or multicellular structure in which gametes are formed.

*Gametophore.* In mosses, the leafy structure on which antheridia and archegonia are borne.

*Gametophyte.* The generally haploid, gamete-producing plant.

*Gemma.* A vegetative reproductive body, such as in liverworts, which becomes detached and develops into a new plant.

*Habitat.* The particular environment where an organism is usually found.

*Haploid.* Having one full chromosome complement per nucleus.

*Haustorium.* A specialized, nutrient-absorbing cell or tissue of parasites.

*Hermaphroditic.* Having both male and female sex organs on one individual.

*Heteroecious.* Requiring two different host species in order to complete its life cycle.

*Heteromorphic.* Having more than one form.

*Heterosporous.* Producing meiospores of two types.

*Heterothallic.* Requiring two different plants for sexual reproduction; may either be unisexual or hermaphroditic (but self-incompatible).

*Heterotrichous.* Differentiated into prostrate, rhizoidal, and erect systems.

*Heterotrophic.* Having energy needed to drive synthetic reactions coming from breakdown of organic compounds; organisms live as parasites or saprobes.

*Holdfast.* In algae, a cell or group of cells that serve to attach the organism to a substrate.

*Homosporous.* Producing meiospores of only one type.

*Homothallic.* Having sexual reproduction on a single thallus; these plants are both hermaphroditic and self-compatible.

*Hydroids.* Water-conducting elements of mosses.

**Glossary**

223

*Hygroscopic.*   Sensitive to moisture.

*Hypha.*   A fungal filament.

*Indusium.*   Leaf tissue that covers a fern sorus.

*Isogamy.*   Sexual fusion in which the gametes are of similar size and form.

*Isomorphic.*   Having one form.

*Leptoid.*   Food-conducting elements of mosses.

*Lysogenic.*   A virus-bacterium relationship in which the viral DNA is carried by the host cell from generation to generation.

*Lytic.*   A virus-host relationship that leads to rapid cell death.

*Mating type.*   Term used for heterothallic organisms in which the sexes cannot visibly be separated.

*Megaspore.*   Meiospore of heterosporous plants that gives rise to the female gametophyte.

*Meiosporangium.*   A unicellular or multicellular structure in which meiosis occurs and in which meiospores develop.

*Meiospore.*   Flagellated or nonflagellated reproductive cell of a plant produced following meiosis.

*Meristem.*   Embryonic tissue of plants capable of cell division and giving rise to other tissues.

*Meristoderm.*   Outer meristematic cell layer of some brown algae.

*Mesosome.*   A localized infolding of the cell membrane of bacteria, suggested to be involved in nucleoid separation during cell growth.

*Microspore.*   Meiospore of heterosporous plants that gives rise to the male gametophyte.

*Mitosporangium.*   A structure in which mitospores develop.

*Mitospore.*   The flagellated or nonflagellated reproductive cell of a plant produced following mitosis.

*Monokaryotic.*   Having a single nucleus, or several nuclei of the same genetic type, in each cell.

*Monophyletic.*   Of a single line of descent.

*Morphogenesis.*   The development of form and structure.

*Mutualism.*   The living together of two or more organisms in close association, in which each organism benefits from the relationship.

*Mycelium.*   The mass of hyphae of a fungus.

*Mycorrhiza.*   Close association between fungal hyphae and roots of vascular plants.

*Nucleoid.*   The bacterial nucleus, in which the DNA is not surrounded by a double unit membrane.

*Ontogeny.*   The development of an individual.

*Oogamy.*   Sexual fusion in which a sperm fuses with a large, nonmotile egg.

*Oogonium.*   Unicellular gametangium in which one or more eggs develop.

*Oospore.*   Thick-walled resting zygote of the Oomycetes.

*Operculum.*  In mosses, the lid at the apex of the capsule; it usually comes off at capsule maturity.

*Palmelloid.*  A transient nonmotile stage in the life histories of many motile algae such as *Chlamydomonas;* the cells become embedded in a gelatinous matrix.

*Parasitism.*  A form of symbiosis in which one organism lives at the expense of the other.

*Parenchyma.*  Tissue of usually thin-walled, isodiametric cells.

*Pellicle.*  The specialized structure of euglenoids that lies between the cell membrane and the protoplast.

*Peristome.*  The mouth of the opened moss capsule; often ringed by tooth-like structures.

*Perithecium.*  A spherical or flask-shaped fruiting body of Ascomycetes, containing an opening.

*Phagocytosis.*  Process of ingestion of solid food particles.

*Phloem.*  The food-conducting tissue of vascular plants.

*Photoautotrophic.*  Capable of utilizing light energy for the synthesis of food from inorganic compounds.

*Phototropism.*  A directional response toward or away from light.

*Phycobilisome.*  Particle associated with thylakoids in red and blue-green algae that contain the red and blue phycobiliproteins, which, in turn, trap light in photosynthesis.

*Phylogeny.*  The historical development or evolutionary history of a group.

*Pit connection.*  Usually refers to the type of septal apparatus in red algae.

*Plankton.*  Generally microscopic floating or flagellated organisms that are readily carried about by water currents.

*Plasmodium.*  A multinucleate mass of naked protoplasm, constituting the predominant vegetative phase of slime molds.

*Plastid.*  A double unit membrane cell organelle involved in the synthesis and/or storage of food; one type is the chloroplast.

*Polymer.*  A large molecule composed of identical or similar units; for example, starch made up of glucose units.

*Polyphyletic.*  Having several lines of descent.

*Prokaryotic.*  Literally, before a nucleus; lacking double unit membrane structures.

*Proplastids.*  Small cell organelles surrounded by a double unit membrane that lack chlorophyll and that are capable of developing into chloroplasts.

*Prothallus.*  Gametophyte of vascular plants and of the moss *Sphagnum.*

*Protonema* (pl. protonemata).  Literally, first thread; in mosses, the filamentous growth phase developing from spore germination.

*Pseudoplasmodium.*  Mass formed from the aggregation of myxamoebae in the cellular slime molds.

*Pseudopodium.*  Literally, a false foot; temporary cytoplasmic extension of a cell.

*Pyrenoid.*  A specialized, proteinaceous part of the chloroplast of many algae and of hornworts, and closely associated with starch synthesis in green algae and hornworts.

*Raphe.*  Unsilicified fissure in the cell wall of some diatoms.

*Respiration.*  In plants, the cellular stepwise anaerobic or aerobic liberation of energy during the breakdown of organic molecules.

*Rhizoid.*  An absorptive and anchorage structure in plants.

*Rhizome.*  Horizontal, usually underground, stem.

*Saprobe.*  An organism that lives on dead organic matter.

*Saprotism.*  The condition of living on dead organic matter.

*Septum* (pl. septa).  A partition or cross wall.

*Seta.*  In mosses, the stalk that bears the sporophyte capsule.

*Sorocarp.*  The spore-forming structure of cellular slime molds.

*Sorus.*  In ferns, a collection of sporangia.

*Sperm.*  A usually flagellated male gamete that can fuse with an egg.

*Spermagonium.*  The structure in which are produced spermatia of fungi such as those in rusts.

*Spermatium.*  Name for the nonflagellated male gamete of red algae and some fungi such as rusts.

*Sporangiophore.*  In sphenopsids, a specialized branch that bears sporangia.

*Sporangiospore.*  A mitospore formed in a sporangium.

*Sporangium.*  A unicellular or multicellular structure in which spores are produced.

*Sporogenous.*  Producing spores.

*Sporophyll.*  A leaf-like appendage that bears or sub-tends sporangia.

*Sporophyte.*  The meiospore-producing plant; generally diploid.

*Stipe.*  A stem-like structure of mushrooms or brown algae.

*Stolon.*  In fungi such as *Rhizopus*, a prostrate filament from which arise rhizoids and sporangiophores.

*Stoma* (pl. stomata).  A microscopic pore, surrounded by guard cells, which facilitates gas exchange between interior tissue of the plant and the atmosphere.

*Strobilus.*  An aggregation of sporangia along a stem into a cone.

*Symbiosis.*  The relationship of two organisms living in close association with each other.

*Syngamy.*  The fusion of gametes.

*Taxon.*  Term used for any taxonomic category, whether it be species, genus, or division.

*Teliospore.*  A thick-walled resting spore in rusts and smuts in which nuclear fusion occurs; gives rise to the basidium.

*Tetraploid.*  Having four full chromosome complements per nucleus.

---

*Tetrasporophyte.*   Diploid (usually free-living) plant in red algae that produces tetra-spores (meiospores).

*Thallus.*   Plant body lacking vascular tissue.

*Thylakoid.*   Flattened, closed lamellar units that contain chlorophyll molecules.

*Uredospore.*   A binucleate spore, formed in rusts, which is capable of reinfecting the same species on which the spore is formed.

*Vascular system.*   Conductive system composed of xylem and phloem.

*Venter.*   Base of the archegonium; contains the egg.

*Virion.*   The mature virus particle.

*Xylem.*   Lignified water-conducting tissue of vascular plants.

*Zoosporangium.*   A sporangium in which flagellated mitospores (zoospores) are produced.

*Zoospore.*   A general term that includes both flagellated mitospores and flagellated meiospores.

*Zygospore.*   Thick-walled resting spore developed following gametangial fusion in the Zygomycetes.

*Zygote.*   A diploid cell formed by fusion of gametes.

# Suggestions for
# Further Reading

Alexopoulos, C. J. *Introductory Mycology*, 2nd ed. New York: John Wiley & Sons, Inc., 1962.

Barghoorn, E. S., and J. W. Schopf. "Microorganisms Three Billion Years Old from the Precambrian of South Africa." *Science*, Vol. 152 (1966), pp. 758–763.

Bartnicki-Garcia, S. "Cell Wall Chemistry, Morphogenesis, and Taxonomy of Fungi." *Annual Review of Microbiology*, Vol. 22 (1968), pp. 87–108.

Bold, H. C. *Morphology of Plants*. 2nd ed. New York: Harper and Row, 1967.

Bonner, J. T. *The Cellular Slime Molds*. Princeton, N.J.: Princeton University Press, 1959.

Bopp, M. "Control of Differentiation in Fern-Allies and Bryophytes." *Annual Review of Plant Physiology*, Vol. 19 (1968), pp. 361–380.

Buetow, D. E., ed. *The Biology of Euglena*. New York: Academic Press, 1968.

Cantino, E. C. "Physiology and Development of Lower Fungi (Phycomycetes)." *Annual Review of Microbiology*, Vol. 13 (1959), pp. 97–124.

Carefoot, G. L., and E. R. Sprott. *Famine on the Wind*. Skokie, Ill.: Rand McNally Press, 1966.

Christensen, C. M. *The Molds and Man*, 2nd ed. Minneapolis: University of Minnesota Press, 1961.

Denison, W. C., and G. C. Carroll. "The Primitive Ascomycete: A New Look at an Old Problem." *Mycologia,* Vol. 58 (1966), pp. 249–269.

Doyle, W. T. *The Biology of Higher Cryptogams.* New York: The Macmillan Company, 1970.

Emerson, R. "The Biology of Water Molds." In *Aspects of Synthesis and Order in Growth.* Princeton, N.J.: Princeton University Press, 1955, pp. 171–208.

Foster, A. S., and E. M. Gifford. *Comparative Morphology of Vascular Plants.* San Francisco: W. H. Freeman and Company, 1959.

Gunsalus, I. C., and R. Y. Stanier, eds. *The Bacteria: A Treatise on Structure and Function.* New York: Academic Press, 1960.

Hale, M. E., Jr. *Lichen Handbook.* Washington: Smithsonian Institution, Publication 4434, 1961.

Ingold, C. T. *Dispersal in Fungi.* Oxford: Clarendon Press, 1953.

Jackson, D. F., ed. *Algae and Man.* New York: Plenum Press, 1964.

Krauss, R. W. "Physiology of the Fresh-Water Algae." *Annual Review of Plant Physiology,* Vol. 9 (1958), pp. 207–244.

Lang, N. J. "The Fine Structure of Blue-green Algae." *Annual Review of Microbiology,* Vol. 22 (1968), pp. 15–46.

Large, E. C. *The Advance of the Fungi.* New York: Henry Holt and Company, 1940.

Lewin, R. A., ed. *Physiology and Biochemistry of the Algae.* New York: Academic Press, 1962.

Margulis, L. "Evolutionary Criteria in Thallophytes: A Radical Alternative." *Science,* Vol. 161 (1968), pp. 1020–1022.

Miller, J. H. "Fern Gametophytes as Experimental Material." *The Botanical Review,* Vol. 34 (1968), pp. 361–440.

Näf, U. "Developmental Physiology of Lower Archegoniates." *Annual Review of Plant Physiology,* Vol. 13 (1962), pp. 507–532.

Nickerson, W. J. "Molecular Basis of Form in Yeasts." Symposium on Biochemical Basis of Morphogenesis in Fungi, IV. *Bacteriological Reviews,* Vol. 27 (1963), pp. 305–324.

Parihar, N. S. *An Introduction to the Embryophyta: I. Bryophyta.* 4th rev. ed. Allahabad, India: Central Book Depot, 1961.

Parihar, N. S. *An Introduction to Embryophyta: II. Pteridophyta.* 2nd rev. ed. Allahabad, India: Central Book Depot, 1957.

Plunkett, B. E. "The Influence of Factors of the Aeration Complex and Light upon Fruit-Body Form in Pure Culture of an Agaric and a Polypore." *Annals of Botany,* Vol. 20 (1956), 563–586.

Pontefract, R. D., G. Bergeron, and F. S. Thatcher. "Mesosomes in *Escherichia coli.*" *Journal of Bacteriology,* Vol. 97 (1969), pp. 367–375.

Pringsheim, E. G. *Pure Cultures of Algae.* New York: Hafner Publishing Company, 1964.

Raper, J. R. "Hormones and Sexuality in Lower Plants." *Symposia of the Society for Experimental Biology,* No. 11 (1957), pp. 143–165.

Raper, J. R. "The Control of Sex in Fungi." *American Journal of Botany,* Vol. 47 (1960), pp. 794–808.

Siegel, S. M., and B. Z. Siegel. "A Living Organism Morphologically Comparable to the Precambrian *Kakabeckia.*" *American Journal of Botany,* Vol. 55 (1968), pp. 684–687.

Smith, A. H. *The Mushroom Hunter's Field Guide.* Ann Arbor: University of Michigan Press, 1960.

Smith, G. M. *The Fresh-Water Algae of the United States.* 2nd. ed. New York: McGraw-Hill Book Company, Inc., 1950.

Smith, G. M., ed. *Manual of Phycology.* Waltham, Mass.: Chronica Botanica, 1951.

Smith, G. M. *Cryptogamic Botany,* 2nd ed. New York: McGraw-Hill Book Company, Inc., 1955.

Sparrow, F. K. *Aquatic Phycomycetes,* 2nd rev. ed. Ann Arbor: University of Michigan Press, 1960.

Verdoorn, F., ed. *Manual of Bryology.* The Hague: M. Nijhoff, 1932.

Watson, E. V. *The Structure and Life of Bryophytes.* London: Hutchinson & Company, Ltd., 1964.

# Index

Alginates, 128, 130, 134
*Allomyces,* 32, 44, 45–47, 50
Alternation of generations:
  heteromorphic, 132, 133, 150, 169, 192, 193
  isomorphic, 131, 132, 150
*Amanita,* 63, 64
Amoebae, 77, 81, 85
*Anabaena,* 99, 104
*Anacystis nidulans,* 101
Anaerobic bacteria, 17, 22, 24, 26, 27
Antheridia:
  Ascomycetes, 55, 56
  Bryophytes, 170, 181
  ferns, 211
  *Fucus,* 134, 136
  *Laminaria,* 134
  Oomycetes, 47, 48
*Anthoceros,* 173
Antibiotics, 23, 29, 38, 43
  algal responses, 101
Aphids, 8
Apothecium, 56
Archegonium, 170, 181, 183, 210, 211
*Arthrobotrys conoides,* 39
Ascocarps, 54, 56, 57, 72
Ascogonium, 55, 56
Ascomycetes, 35, 44, 53–60, 63, 72, 116
Ascospores 57–59
Ascus, 57–60
Asexual reproduction, 33, 38, 47, 48, 49, 50, 54, 60, 119, 132, 163
Aspartic acid, 31, 32
*Aspergillus,* 54, 55
*Astasia,* 146
ATP, 77
Autotrophism, 22, 26
Auxospore, 124
Axenic culture, 17
*Azobacter,* 26

Bacillariophyceae, *see* Diatoms
Bacilli, 16
Bacteria, 1, 4, 5, 8, 16–28, 70, 76, 89, 90, 91, 101, 102, 107, 147
  cellular structure, 17–22

Bacteria (continued)
  nitrogen cycle, 25–27
  nutritional modes, 22–27
  population growth curve, 20, 21
  resemblances to algae, 107
  virus infections of, 11–16
Bacteriology, 16
Bacteriophages, 11–16
  $T_2$, 12
  $T_4$, 11, 12, 13, 14
Barberry plant, common, 65, 68
Basal disc, 83
Basidiocarp, 63, 64
Basidiomycetes, 36, 44, 53, 60–70, 72
Basidiospores, 60, 62, 65, 68
Basidium, 60, 62, 68
*Batrachospermum,* 114, 115
Bleached cells, 146, 147
Bordeaux mixture, 38
Botanical classification, 2, 3
Botulism, 22
Brewer's yeast, 35, 59, 60
Bryophytes, 1, 169–192, 197
  attributes, 169, 170
  distribution, 170, 171
  gametophores, 177–184
  gametophytes, 172–177, 181, 189
  sporophytes, 171, 172, 183, 184–192
Budding, 59, 60
*Buxbaumia,* 185

Callose, 170
*Calvatia,* 64
Calyptra, 183–184
Capsid, 9, 10, 11, 13
Capsule, 20
Carbon cycle, 23
Carbon dioxide, 89
  effect on cellular metabolism, 31
Carboniferous period, 197, 200, 207
Carotenoids, 4, 94, 130, 146
Carpogonium, 113, 114, 115, 116
Carposporangia, 115
Carpospores, 115
Carposporophyte, 115, 116
*Carteria,* 158
*Catenaria,* 30

Universal veil, 64
Uredospore, 66, 67, 68

Vacuoles, 20
Vascular plants, 170 ff., 193 ff.
    *see also* Fern allies; Ferns
Vascular system, 207, 209
*Vaucheria,* 71, 117, 118, 125
Virion, 8–10, 11, 12
Virus, 7–16, 107
    bacteriophagic, 8, 11–16
    Tobacco Mosaic, 8, 9, 10
    *see also* Virus
Vitamin B$_{12}$, 91, 143
Volvox, 91, 93, 163

"Water-squirt" mechanism, 51
Wheat rust, *see Puccinia graminis*

Woronin body, 54

Xanthophyta, *see* Algae, yellow-green
Xylem, 170

Yeast, 20, 29, 31, 76
Yeast, brewer's, *see* Brewer's yeast

*Zonaria,* 96
Zooplankton, 92
Zoosporangia, 47
Zoospores, 32, 33
*Zygnema,* 93
Zygomycetes, 49–53, 71, 72
Zygospores, 33, 51
Zygote, 33, 87
Zygote formation, 45, 134